REPLACING

4

THE SEARCH PARTY

George A. Birmingham

THE SEARCH
PARTY

WITH AN INTRODUCTION BY

William Trevor

THE BODLEY HEAD
LONDON SYDNEY
TORONTO

INTRODUCTION

NOVELISTS create worlds: the Dickens world, the world of Jane Austen, Cranford, Brickfield Terrace. They're private, exclusive worlds, with laws and language of their own, populated by people who are at one with their environment and could healthily live in no other. Pickwick in Hartfield would be a silent fellow and Emma would feel as uneasy in The Laurels as Bertie Wooster would in the presence of Buck Mulligan. Nor would one care to contemplate the fate of Widmerpool in Greeneland. It is that sense of people being right for the world around them, whether it's Wonderland, Ruritania, Nighttown or anywhere else, that gives good fiction its gloss of success. It's a sense of correctness and aptness, painlessly achieved when the novelist's world grows naturally from seeds of reality.

The world of George A. Birmingham is one man's picture of Ireland, etched over a period of forty years from the beginning of this century. It is a picture that does not go in much for sombre tones: the lighter side of Irish life, you might say, and note that the world of Somerville and Ross is a nearish neighbour and that of Dorothea Conyers just over the horizon.

As a child in provincial Ireland I lived within the reality of the Birmingham world, a reality that has since changed in many superficial ways, as Ireland itself has changed. I remember Birmingham people: old Zeb Millar, a canon of the Church of Ireland who was said to eat only Fox's Glacier Mints, and Sergeant Bevan driven demented down in the barracks trying to learn Irish, and young Ned Watson who used to swim miles out to sea, his red head bobbing on the waves, and a chimney sweep who was small enough to go up the chimneys

5

himself and once was up there when our maid, Kitty, lit a fire. Ned Watson became a Church of Ireland curate: he could easily have been the adventuring cleric of *Spanish Gold*.

Between 1903 and 1950 hardly a year went by without a new book from George Birmingham; often he produced two, or even three, a year, and all he published was eagerly lapped up. The critics enjoyed him, too. The *Morning Post* said: 'Mr Birmingham of *Spanish Gold* has given us more entertainment than any living humorist except Mr W. W. Jacobs.' 'Pure undiluted humour,' was the view of the *Morning Leader*. 'Irresistible,' agreed the *Manchester Guardian*. Readers escaped with Birmingham. They loved his 'exquisite fooling', and no doubt appreciated that a Birmingham journey wasn't just any old joy-ride: he was a master at what he set out to do and as an exquisite fooler he's had, since his day, only a small handful of rivals.

His real name was James Owen Hannay. He was born in Belfast in 1865 and died in London in 1950. Educated at Haileybury and Trinity College, Dublin, he became a Church of Ireland curate himself, serving first in Co. Wicklow and later, as rector, in Westport, Co. Mayo. During the First World War he was a chaplain with the British Army in France and in 1922 became chaplain of the British Legation in Budapest. He was rector of Wells from 1924 to 1934 and then of Holy Trinity Church, Kensington. He married Ada Wynne, daughter of the Bishop of Killaloe, and was the father of two sons and two daughters. Such background information is relevant: Birmingham, like Somerville and Ross, was of the class, religion and political stance that attract the label 'Anglo-Irish'. It's a label that complicates matters: the Irish, always touchy about being laughed at, burnt him in effigy as a Protestant whose jokes were sometimes too much of a good thing.

His work was regarded as part of the long-established Ascendancy and, when Ascendancy was gone, as echoes of it. His play, *General John Regan*, caused rioting when it was

6

first produced in Westport: the same welcome that was to greet Synge's *Playboy of the Western World* in the Abbey, and much of O'Casey. In fact, the Westport rioters, like the Abbey ones, had got hold of the wrong end of the stick: he was on their side.

His affection for the people he wrote about, while not always apparent in the heat of those revolutionary times, is certainly apparent today. These people of rural Ireland—the sleeping officers of a small-town police barracks, the priest jealously guarding his flock, the crafty traders and hotel-keepers, the Land League supporters, the Union-Jack opponents of all change—are presented by Birmingham with a great deal more good in them than bad. Pomposity and pretension, carried into the Birmingham world by luckless outsiders, are the bubbles that are regularly and delightedly pricked, because for all his apparent cheerfulness he was an exceedingly sharp man. An extrovert who liked nothing better than messing about in sailing-boats or chatting for long gossipy hours in the Royal Irish Yacht Club, who claimed for his work no great literary merit, he still observed his fellow creatures with the steely see-through gaze of the novelist who knows precisely what he's up to. Wrong end of the stick or not, it isn't blarney that causes people to riot in a theatre.

Spanish Gold is a story about a search for buried treasure on an island. But what might with a lesser writer have been a fairly simple and ordinary yarn is transformed by Birmingham into a complicated and witty romp. It's a classic of its kind, and the Rev. J. J. Meldon, constantly indulging his partiality for hard liquor and his capacity for telling lies, is a man worth knowing. So is Dr Lucius O'Grady, the hero of *The Search Party*, who happens to be a fairly useful liar also. As with other well-made heroes of adventure fiction—Richard Hannay, Percy Blakeney, Bulldog Drummond with his rough code of behaviour and his sadistic streak, Peter Wimsey, Ross Macdonald's Lew Archer—Birmingham's leading men were built to last. They have done so to the extent that beside them

7

such 'pretend' figures as James Bond and his ilk look like nothing so much as words on paper. The Birmingham heroes are carefully established as people who breathe and eat and have ordinary human strengths and weaknesses, which means that when a plot takes an outlandish turn, as the plots of adventure stories tend to, credibility isn't as strained as it might be. With real human beings, you can get away with murder.

The plot, for instance, of *The Search Party* could be considered by some to be particularly outlandish, and a suggestion towards the end of it made by Jimmy O'Loughlin, proprietor of the Imperial Hotel in Clonmore, might seem to be the final outlandish straw. But O'Loughlin is no strip-cartoon figure, and I can personally vouch for the fact that such suggestions are not at all uncommon in the Irish provinces. There was Mrs Driscoll's for a start, the night the hypnotist got into difficulties with Mr McGrath. But let's begin with *The Search Party*.

A stranger called Mr Red rents a house near the village of Clonmore in Western Connacht, the only tenant Lord Manton ever had who didn't ask finicky questions about the drainage. With Mr Red are two foreign companions, an English servant, and twenty-five packing-cases. There is speculation about whether these contain pianos, machinery or blocks of marble for a statue, and about whether Mr Red is a revolutionary, a sculptor, or a composer of operas.

Having established this small mystery, Birmingham swiftly gets down to business. Dr O'Grady disappears. A man called Patsy Devlin disappears. Miss Blow, the doctor's fiancée, arrives from England. So do two English Members of Parliament and their wives. These men also disappear, leaving their wives behind them.

Pandemonium ensues in Clonmore. The bereft wives weep and fuss. Miss Blow, composed of sterner stuff, gathers together her search party, intent on the house of Mr Red. Two men of approximately the same description as the missing

M.P.s are reported to be on the steamer *Rose* en route from Derry to Glasgow, but they prove not to be the right men. Dr O'Grady, Patsy Devlin and the M.P.s seem now, to everyone in Clonmore except Miss Blow and the wives, to be gone for ever, and understandably so. Didn't the doctor owe money left, right and centre? And aren't Patsy Devlin and the M.P.s only escaping from the demands of their nearest and dearest, as any decent men might now and again desire to?

The rest of the plot looks after itself, but not before Jimmy O'Loughlin has made his suggestion: since the bereft wives show no sign of ceasing their commotion, and since the two men on the steamer *Rose* are apparently similar to the missing men, wouldn't it be an idea to ask the Glasgow police to send these travellers over? Provided they were a decent type of man, why wouldn't they be a comfort to the wives? And in any case, comfort or not, wouldn't they be better than nothing at all?

That it's hard to imagine a pair of deserted women accepting two strangers off a steamer in place of their legally attached husbands is beside the point. Jimmy O'Loughlin was hardly to know what English women, with whom he was only slightly acquainted, would or would not get up to in terms of men on cross-channel steamers. And in any case no one had a better suggestion, or indeed a suggestion of any kind. Which brings me back to Mrs Driscoll.

A hypnotist from Dublin, displaying his talents in the cinema of our Co. Tipperary town, enticed on to the stage the local hardware merchant, a Mr McGrath. The hypnotist, a small, shrill man, then persuaded Mr McGrath that he was a fowl, a steel girder, and Mr McGrath's own dog, an animal called Esso. Mr McGrath, a bulkier man than the hypnotist, middle-aged and unmarried, with a warm red face and a moustache, had been in Kelly's Bar with John Joe Ryan since half-past five: all inhibitions gone, he entered his trances like an infant. Obediently he pecked bits of dirt off the boards of the stage, rooting about like a hen. He stretched himself out between one chair and another and didn't give way when the hypnotist walked across him. He barked like the dog called Esso, a greyhound that was locally considered not to be sane. The hypnotist was naturally delighted. He'd had trouble with several youths who'd pretended to be entranced and had mooed like cattle when he'd wanted them to make grasshopper sounds. He'd also had trouble with John Joe Ryan. But Mr McGrath made up for all that: Mr McGrath was the goods, and it was with Mr McGrath's co-operation that he intended to offer us the climax of his show, his *pièce de résistance*. 'Isn't he the right little divil?' said Mrs Driscoll, a stout, good-hearted woman who worked part-time in Phelan's Drapery.

The hypnotist seated the hardware merchant comfortably and coaxed him into the deepest trance of the evening. He then persuaded Mr McGrath that he was a weather-cock, and like the Pied Piper he led the unconscious hardware merchant and everyone else out of the cinema, down North Street, to the Protestant church. In the moonlight, ladders were provided for Mr McGrath's ascent. (It was explained to the hypnotist that Mr McGrath, being a Catholic, would have scruples about entering a heretical building and so could not be expected to make his way up the interior of the church tower.)

Up Mr McGrath went and on the street below an awed silence broke into a murmur of wonder. 'Holy Mary herself, will you look at him!' cried Mrs Driscoll, and Ellie Power, who was said to have hopes of getting Mr McGrath to an altar, had to sit down on the bonnet of a car. 'That's the end of McGrath,' remarked John Joe Ryan, a statement that caused Ellie Power to make a moaning noise. But the hardware merchant reached the top of the tower without incident, clambered over the turrets and took up a position near the flagpole. Clapping broke out below, and people shook the hypnotist by the hand. Big men struck him companionably across the shoulder-blades.

Unfortunately, events now took an unexpected turn. The

hypnotist called for silence and then shouted up at Mr McGrath, informing him that he wasn't a weather-cock but Joseph Tom McGrath. The crowd waited in pleasurable anticipation, ready to cry out with delight when Mr McGrath came to his senses and found himself on top of the Protestant church at ten o'clock on a sharp November night. But Mr McGrath continued to stand in the position he'd taken up. 'You're Joseph Tom McGrath,' shouted the hypnotist. 'You're de Valera,' shouted John Joe Ryan, and Ellie Power again made a moaning noise.

The hypnotist climbed the ladder and after a conversation with Mr McGrath slowly climbed down again. 'I can't get through to him,' he reported, and at once there occurred the kind of pandemonium that occurred in the village of Clonmore when its men began to disappear. Ellie Power had to be assisted, Mrs Driscoll again called on the Holy Mother, and John Joe Ryan said wasn't it a terrible place to die, the roof of a Protestant church? Father Daly, who had been dubious all along about the presence of a hypnotist in the town and had only attended the entertainment in the cinema to keep an eye on the morals of the occasion, said that he felt it his duty personally to address the hardware merchant. He climbed the ladder with the hypnotist behind him and John Joe Ryan and another man behind the hypnotist. But within a quarter of an hour this small party was on the street again, having failed in its mission. Nothing would budge Mr McGrath. 'It's never happened to me before,' said the hypnotist, but nobody listened to him.

Gloom descended on the people of the town, for Mr McGrath was a respected and well-liked citizen, and even if he came out of the trance, the doubt now was that he'd ever be the same again. 'Afflicted for life,' said John Joe Ryan, 'like that poor old dog of his.' Again the hypnotist mounted the ladder and again somewhat shakily descended it. No man on earth could budge Mr McGrath, he said.

It was then, perhaps inspired by these words, that Mrs

Driscoll made her suggestion. Couldn't the hypnotist persuade Major Dwyer's foxhounds that they'd got the scent of a fox that had climbed to the tower of the Protestant church? The hounds could be let into the church and could go up the inside of the tower, the Major being a Protestant and the hounds presumably the same. 'They'd have him down that ladder in one half-second,' said Mrs Driscoll. 'Wouldn't they, Father?'

But Father Doyle forbade the use of foxhounds and told Mrs Driscoll not to be ridiculous in much the same way as Jimmy O'Loughlin was told not to be ridiculous in George Birmingham's story. In time Mr McGrath came down from the tower of his own free will, and appeared to be perfectly normal the following day.

The simple point is that beneath all the normality of lace curtains and porter and Mass and hurling matches eccentric events do tend to occur in small Irish towns, and the talk that goes with them is often as wild as Goon-talk. Language is shaped by a craziness which has nothing to do with the darker depths of madness but which, through a misty Celtic twilight, has often been seen as the inspiration of an art-form. Birmingham skipped the earnestness and celebrated instead the fun of the thing, delighting in the truths of the absurd without paying them too much intellectual attention. His play (and novel) *General John Regan*, in which a statue is erected to the memory of a man who never existed, is totally extraordinary and yet credible from start to finish: farcically, but perfectly, it represents the contradiction-in-terms that Ireland and the Irish so often are.

In Ireland today there is, understandably, very little laughter in novels, short stories and plays. If only for that reason and no other, it's good to enter again the George Birmingham world, to be reminded that Ireland, for all its tragedy, can be happily funny too. It's good to laugh and often to marvel, to share in an endless flow of enthusiasm for the comic, and constantly to sense the gentleness of a writer who loved his people.

WILLIAM TREVOR

I

———◦◎◦———

Dr O'Grady, Dr Lucius O'Grady, was the medical officer
of the Poor Law Union of Clonmore, which is in Western
Connacht. The office is not like that of resident magistrate or
bank manager. It does not necessarily confer on its holder the
right of entry to the highest society. Therefore, Dr O'Grady
was not invited to dinner, luncheon, or even afternoon tea by
Lord Manton at that season of the year when Clonmore Castle
was full of visitors. Lady Flavia Canning, Lord Manton's
daughter, who was married to a London barrister of some
distinction, and moved in smart society, did not appreciate
Dr O'Grady. Nor did those nephews and nieces of the
deceased Lady Manton who found it convenient to spend a
part of each summer at Clonmore Castle. They were not the
sort of people who would associate with a dispensary doctor,
unless, indeed, he had possessed a motor car. And Dr
O'Grady, for reasons which became obvious later on, did not
keep a motor car.

On the other hand, he was a frequent guest at the Castle
during those early summer months when Lord Manton was
alone. In April and May, for instance, and in June, Dr
O'Grady dined once, twice, or even three times a week at
Clonmore Castle. The old earl liked him because he found
him amusing; and Dr O'Grady had a feeling for his host as
nearly approaching respect as it was in his nature to entertain
for any man. This respect was not of the kind which every
elderly earl would have appreciated. The doctor was con-
stitutionally incapable of understanding the innate majesty
of a peerage, and had not the smallest veneration for grey

13

hairs in man or woman. Nor was he inclined to bow before any moral superiority in Lord Manton. In fact, Lord Manton, though grown too old for the lavish wildness of his earlier years, made no pretence at morality or dignity of any kind. What Dr O'Grady respected and liked in him was a certain cynical frankness, a hinted contempt for all ordinary standards of respectability. This suited well enough the doctor's own volatile indifference to anything which threatened to bore him.

When Lord Manton returned to Clonmore in May, 1905, after his usual visit to his daughter in Grosvenor Street, he at once asked Dr O'Grady to dinner. There was on this occasion a special reason for the invitation, though doubtless it would have been given and accepted without any reason. Lord Manton wanted to know all that could be known about a new tenant who had taken Rosivera for six months. Rosivera, long used as a dower house by Lord Manton's ancestors, was not an easy place to let. It stood eight miles from the village of Clonmore, on the shore of a small land-locked bay. It was a singularly unattractive building, rectangular, grey, four storeys high, and lit by small ineffective windows. There was no shooting connected with it nor any fishing of the kind appreciated by a sportsman. There were, it was believed, small flat fish to be caught in the bay, but no one thought it worth while to pursue these creatures earnestly. Occasionally an adventurous Englishman, cherishing some romantic idea of the west of Ireland, rented the house for August and September. Occasionally a wealthy Dublin doctor brought his family there for six weeks. None of these tenants ever came a second time. The place was too solitary for the social, too ugly for the amateurs of the picturesque, utterly dull for the sportsman, and had not even the saving grace of an appeal to the romantic. The mother and grandmother of Lord Manton had died there, but in the odour of moderate sanctity. Their ghosts wandered down no corridors. Indeed, no ghosts could have haunted, no tradition attached itself to a house with the shape and appearance of Rosivera.

There was, therefore, something interesting and curious in the fact that a tenant had taken the place for six months and had settled down there early in March, a time of year at which even a hermit, vowed to a life entirely devoid of incident, might have hesitated to fix his cell at Rosivera.

'The first thing that struck me as queer about the man,' said Lord Manton, after dinner, 'was his name. Did you ever hear of anybody called Red? Scarlett, of course, is comparatively common.'

'So is Black,' said Dr O'Grady, 'and Brown, and Grey, and White. I've heard of Pink, and I once met a man called Blue, but he spelt it "ew".'

'Guy Theodore Red is this man's name. Guy and Theodore are all right, of course, but Red——!'

'Is he safe for the rent, do you think?'

'He has paid the whole six months in advance,' said Lord Manton, 'and he never asked a question about the drains. He's the only tenant I ever heard of who didn't make himself ridiculous about drains.'

'He hasn't got typhoid yet,' said Dr O'Grady. 'If he's the kind of man who pays six months' rent in advance and asks no questions, I hope he soon will.'

'Unfortunately for you he seems to have neither wife nor children.'

'No, nor as much as a maid-servant,' said Dr O'Grady. 'And from the look of him, I'd say he was a tough old cock himself, the sort of man a microbe would hesitate about attacking.'

'You've seen him, then?'

'I happened to be standing at Jimmy O'Loughlin's door the day he drove through in his motor car.'

'You would be, of course.'

'But I've never seen him since. Nobody has. He has a servant, an Englishman, I'm told, who comes into the village every second day in the motor, and buys what's wanted for the house at Jimmy O'Loughlin's.'

'Jimmy makes a good thing out of that, I expect,' said Lord Manton.

'Believe you me, he does. Jimmy's the boy who knows how to charge, and these people don't seem to care what they pay.'

'I hear he has two friends with him.'

'He has, foreigners, both of them. Jimmy O'Loughlin says they can't either of them speak English. It was Jimmy who carted their things down to Rosivera from the station, so of course he'd know.'

'Byrne told me that,' said Lord Manton, chuckling as he spoke. 'There seems to have been some queer things to be carted.'

The conversation turned on Mr Red's belongings, the personal luggage which the English servant had brought in the train, the packing-cases which had followed the next day and on many subsequent days. Byrne, it appeared, had also met Mr Red and his party on their arrival; but, then, Byrne had a legitimate excuse wherewith to cover his curiosity. He was Lord Manton's steward, and it was his business to put the new tenant in possession of Rosivera. He had given a full report of Mr Red, the foreign friends and the English servant, to Lord Manton. He had described the packing-cases which, day after day, were carted from the railway station by Jimmy O'Loughlin. They were, according to Byrne, of unusual size and great weight. There were altogether twenty-five of them. It was Byrne's opinion that they contained pianos. The station-master, who had to drag them out of the train, agreed with him. Jimmy O'Loughlin and his man, who had ample opportunities of examining them on the way to Rosivera, thought they were full of machinery, possibly steam engines, or as they expressed it, 'the makings of some of them motor cars'.

'No man,' said Lord Manton, commenting on this information, 'even if his name happens to be Red, can possibly want twenty-five grand pianos in Rosivera.'

'Unless he came down here with the intention of composing an opera,' said Dr O'Grady.

16

'Even then—three, four, anything up to six I could understand, but twenty-five! No opera could require that. As for
those cases containing steam engines or bits of motor cars,
what on earth could a manufacturer of such things be doing
at Rosivera?'

'My own belief,' said Dr O'Grady, 'is that the man is an
artist—a sculptor, engaged in the production of a statue of
unusual size.'

'With blocks of marble in the packing-cases?'

'Yes, and the two foreigners for models. They look like
models. One of them had a long black beard, and the other
was a big man, well over six foot, blond, seemed to be a Norwegian; not that I ever saw a Norwegian to my knowledge,
but this fellow looked like the kind of man a Norwegian
ought to be.'

'It will be a pretty big statue, said Lord Manton, 'if it
absorbs twenty-five blocks of marble, each the size of a grand
piano.'

'He looked like an artist,' said Dr O'Grady; 'he had a
pointed beard, and a wild expression in his eye.'

'A genius escaped from somewhere, perhaps.'

'He very well might be. Indeed, I'd say from the glimpse I
had of him that he's worse than a genius. He had the eye of a
mad gander. But, of course, I only saw him the once, sitting
in his motor, the day he arrived. He hasn't stirred out of
Rosivera since, and, as I said before, I haven't been sent for to
attend him for anything.'

'The queerest thing about him was the message he sent me,'
said Lord Manton. 'By way of doing the civil thing, I told
Byrne to say that I should make a point of calling on him as
soon as I got home.'

'And he sent you word that he'd be thankful if you'd stay
away and not bother him. I heard all about that. Byrne was
furious. That is just one of the things which makes me feel
sure he's a genius. Nobody except a genius or a socialist would
have sent a message of that kind to you; and he clearly isn't

a socialist. If he was, he couldn't afford to pay six months' rent in advance for Rosivera.'

Dr O'Grady spoke confidently. He was not personally acquainted with any of the numerous men of genius in Ireland, but he had read about them in newspapers and was aware that they differed in many respects from other men. No ordinary man, that is to say, no one who is perfectly sane, would refuse to receive a visit from an earl. Mr Red had refused, and so, since he was not a socialist, he must be a genius. The reasoning was perfectly convincing.

'I expect,' said Lord Manton, 'that his statue, in spite of its immense size, will be a melancholy object to look at. Rosivera is the most depressing place I know. It was built to serve as a dower house by my grandfather, and he evidently chose the site and the style of architecture with a view to making his widow feel really sorry he was dead. If I had a wife whom I disliked intensely I should try to die at once so that she should have as long a time as possible to live at Rosivera.'

'I wouldn't care to spend a winter alone there,' said Dr O'Grady, 'and I'm a man of fairly cheerful disposition.'

'I suppose there's a lot of talk about Red in the village?'

'There was at first; but the people are getting a bit sick of him now. It's a long time since he's done anything the least exciting. About a fortnight after he came he sent a telegram which had the whole place fizzing for awhile.'

Telegrams in the west of Ireland, are, of course, public property. So are postcards and the contents of the parcels carried by his Majesty's mails. Lord Manton, whose taste for the details of local gossip was strongly developed, asked what Mr Red's telegram was about.

'That's what nobody could tell,' said Dr O'Grady. 'It began with four letters, A.M.B.A., and then came a lot of figures. Father Moroney worked at it for the best part of two hours, with the help of a Latin dictionary, but he could make no more out of it than I could myself.'

'Cipher,' said Lord Manton; 'probably quite a simple cipher if you'd known how to go about reading it.'

'At the end of the week, another packing-case arrived, carriage paid from London. It was as big as any of the first lot. Byrne and I went up to the station to see it before Jimmy O'Loughlin carted it down to Rosivera. He seemed to think that it was another piano. Since then nothing of any sort has happened, and the people have pretty well given over talking about the man.'

Lord Manton yawned. Like the other inhabitants of Clonmore he was beginning to get tired of Mr Red and his affairs. A stranger is only interesting when there are things about him which can be found out. If his affairs are public property he becomes commonplace and dull. If, on the other hand, it is manifestly impossible to discover anything about him, if he sends his telegrams in cipher, employs a remarkably taciturn servant to do his marketing, and never appears in public himself, he becomes in time quite as tiresome as the man who has no secrets at all.

'Any other news about the place?' asked Lord Manton. 'You needn't mention Jimmy O'Loughlin's wife's baby. Byrne told me about it.'

'It's the tenth,' said Dr O'Grady, 'the tenth boy.'

'So I believe.'

'Well, there's nothing else, except the election of the inspector of sheep dipping. I needn't tell you that there's been plenty of talk about that.'

'So I gathered,' said Lord Manton, 'from the number of candidates for the post who wrote to me asking me to back them up. I think there were eleven of them.'

'I hear that you supported Patsy Devlin, the smith. He's a drunken blackguard.'

'That's why I wrote him the letter of recommendation. There's a lot of stupid talk nowadays about the landlords having lost all their power in the country. It's not a bit true. They have plenty of power, more than they ever had, if they only knew how to use it. All I have to do if I want a particular man not to be appointed to anything is to write a strong letter in his favour to the Board of Guardians or the County Council, or whatever body is doing the particular job that happens to be on hand at the time. The League comes down on my man at once and he hasn't the ghost of a chance. That's the beauty of being thoroughly unpopular. Three years ago you were made dispensary doctor here chiefly because I used all my influence on behalf of the other two candidates. They were both men with bad records. It was just the same in this sheep-dipping business. I didn't care who was appointed so long as it wasn't Patsy Devlin. I managed the labourers' cottages on the same principle. There were two different pieces of land where I particularly objected to their building cottages. I offered them those two without waiting to be asked. Of course, they wouldn't have them, insisted in fact on getting another bit of land altogether, thinking they were annoying me. I was delighted. That's the way to manage things nowadays.'

'Do you suppose,' said Dr O'Grady, 'that if I wrote to Mr Red saying I sincerely hoped he wouldn't get typhoid for a fortnight, because I wanted to go away for a holiday—do you suppose he'd get it to spite me?'

'That's the worst of men in your profession. You're always wanting everybody to be ill. It's most unchristian.'

'I want Red to get typhoid,' said Dr O'Grady, 'because he's the only man in the neighbourhood except yourself who would pay me for curing him.'

2

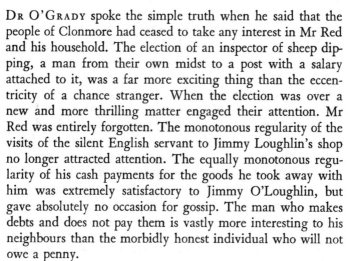

DR O'GRADY spoke the simple truth when he said that the people of Clonmore had ceased to take any interest in Mr Red and his household. The election of an inspector of sheep dipping, a man from their own midst to a post with a salary attached to it, was a far more exciting thing than the eccentricity of a chance stranger. When the election was over a new and more thrilling matter engaged their attention. Mr Red was entirely forgotten. The monotonous regularity of the visits of the silent English servant to Jimmy Loughlin's shop no longer attracted attention. The equally monotonous regularity of his cash payments for the goods he took away with him was extremely satisfactory to Jimmy O'Loughlin, but gave absolutely no occasion for gossip. The man who makes debts and does not pay them is vastly more interesting to his neighbours than the morbidly honest individual who will not owe a penny.

Dr O'Grady owed a good deal, and just at the time of Lord Manton's return to Clonmore, his money difficulties reached the point at which they began to attract public attention. Like most good-humoured and easy-going men, Dr O'Grady lived beyond his income. There was a good deal of excuse for him. He enjoyed, as dispensary doctor, a salary of £120 a year. He received from Lord Manton an additional £30 for looking after the health of the gardeners, grooms, indoor servants and others employed about Clonmore Castle. He would have been paid extra guineas for attending Lord Manton himself if the old gentleman had ever been ill. He could count with tolerable certainty on two pounds a year for ushering into the world young O'Loughlins. Nobody else in his district ever paid him anything.

It is unquestionably possible to live on £152 a year. Many men, curates for instance, live on less; face the world in tolerably clean collars and succeed in looking as if they generally had enough to eat. But Dr O'Grady was not the kind of man who enjoys small economies, and he had certain expensive tastes. He liked to have a good horse between the shafts of a smart trap when he went his rounds. He liked to see the animal's coat glossy and the harness shining. He preferred good whisky to bad, and smoked tobacco at 10s. 6d. a pound. He was particular about the cut of his clothes and had a fine taste in striped and spotted waistcoats. He also—quite privately, for in the west of Ireland no one would admit that he threw away his money wantonly—bought a few books every year. The consequence was inevitable. Dr O'Grady got into debt. At first, indeed for more than two years, his debts, though they increased rapidly, did not cause any uneasiness to his creditors. Then a suspicious tailor began to press rudely for the payment of a long account. Other tradesmen, all of them strangers who did not know Dr O'Grady personally, followed the tailor's example. A Dublin gentleman of large fortune and philanthropic tastes, a Mr Lorraine Vavasour, having somehow heard of these embarrassments, offered to lend Dr O'Grady any sum from £10 to £1000 privately, without security, and on the understanding that repayment should be made quite at the borrower's convenience.

There was an agreeable settlement with the tailor who lost Dr O'Grady's custom for ever, and with several others. Life for a time was pleasant and untroubled. Then Mr Lorraine Vavasour began to act unreasonably. His ideas of the payment of instalments turned out to be anything but suitable to Dr O'Grady's convenience. The good horse was sold at a loss. The competent groom was replaced by an inferior and cheaper man. Mr Lorraine Vavasour showed no signs of being propitiated by these sacrifices. He continued to harass his victim with a persistency which would have made most men miserable and driven some men to excessive drinking. Dr O'Grady remained perfectly cheerful. He had the temperament of an unconquerable optimist. He used even to show Mr Vavasour's worst letters to Jimmy O'Loughlin, and make jokes about them. This, as it turned out afterwards, was an unwise thing to do. Jimmy himself had a long account against the doctor standing in his books.

After awhile the miserable screw which succeeded the good horse in Dr O'Grady's stable was sold. The smart trap and harness were sold. The incompetent substitute for the groom was dismissed. Dr O'Grady endeavoured to do his work with no better means of getting about than a dilapidated bicycle. It was greatly known that his affairs had reached a crisis. His housekeeper left him and engaged a solicitor to write letters in the hope of obtaining the wages due to her. It seemed very unlikely that she would get them. Mr Lorraine Vavasour was before her with a claim which the furniture of Dr O'Grady's house would certainly not satisfy. Jimmy O'Loughlin was before her too. He would have been willing enough to wait for years, and if left to himself would not have driven a friend to extremities for the sake of a few pounds. But when he saw that Mr Vavasour meant to use all the resources of the law against Dr O'Grady he thought it a pity to let a complete stranger get the little there was to get. He apologized to Dr O'Grady and summoned him before the County Court judge. The usual things happened. The end appeared to be at hand, and the Board of Guardians began to discuss the appointment of a new dispensary doctor.

It is very much to the credit of Dr O'Grady that, under these circumstances, he slept soundly at night in his solitary house; rose cheerful in the morning and met his fellow-men with a smile on his face. He continued to dine frequently at Clonmore Castle, and Lord Manton noticed that his appetite improved instead of failing as his troubles increased. In fact, Dr O'Grady frequently went hungry at this time, and Lord

Manton's dinners were almost the only solid meals he got. Then, just before the bailiffs took possession of his house a curious way of escape opened. It was at the beginning of August. Dr O'Grady spent the evening reading a new book about germ plasm, pan-genesis, determinates, and other interesting things connected with the study of heredity. He was obliged to go to bed early because his lamp went out at ten o'clock and he had no oil with which to refill it. Once in bed he went comfortably to sleep. At two o'clock in the morning he was roused by a ponderous, measured knocking at his door. He used the sort of language commonly employed by doctors who are roused at unseemly hours. The knocking continued, a series of heavy detached blows, struck slowly at regular intervals. Dr O'Grady got up, put his head out of the window, and made the usual inquiry—

'Who the devil's that? And what do you want?'

'It is I. Guy Theodore Red.'

Even then, freshly roused from sleep, Dr O'Grady was struck by the answer he received. Very few men, in search of a doctor at two o'clock in the morning, are so particular about grammar as to say, 'It is I!' And the words were spoken in a solemn tone which seemed quite congruous with the measured and stately manner in which the door had been hammered. Dr O'Grady put on a pair of trousers and a shirt, ran downstairs and opened the door. Mr Red stood rigid like a soldier at attention on the doorstep. In the middle of the road was the motor car in which the English servant used to drive into Clanmore to do his marketing.

'Is it typhoid?' said Dr O'Grady; 'for if it is I ought to have been sent for sooner.'

'No.'

'It can't be a midwifery case in your house?'

'No.'

'You're very uncommunicative,' said Dr O'Grady. 'What is it?'

'A gun accident.'

'Very well. Why couldn't you have said so before? Wait a minute.'

Dr O'Grady hurried into his surgery, collected a few instruments likely to be useful, some lint, iodoform, and other things. He stuffed these into a bag, slipped on a few more clothes and an overcoat. Then he left the house. He found Mr Red sitting bolt upright in the motor car with his hands on the steering wheel. Dr O'Grady got in beside him. During the drive Mr Red did not speak a single word. He did not even answer questions. Dr O'Grady was left entirely to his own thoughts. The fresh air had thoroughly awakened him, and, being naturally a man of active mind, he thought a good deal. It occurred to him at once that though gun accidents are common enough in the daytime they very rarely occur in the middle of the night. Good men go to bed before twelve o'clock, and no men, either good or bad, habitually clean guns or go out shooting between midnight and two a.m. Dr O'Grady began to wonder how the accident had happened. It also struck him that Mr Red's manners were peculiar. The man showed no sign of excitement. He was not exactly rude. He was not so far as Dr O'Grady could judge, in a bad temper. He was simply pompous, more pompous than any one whom Dr O'Grady had ever met before. He seemed to be obsessed with an idea of his own enormous importance.

The impression was not removed when the car drew up at Rosivera. Mr Red blew three slow blasts on the horn, stepped out of the car, stalked up to the door, and then stood, as he had stood in front of Dr O'Grady's house, upright, rigid, his arms stretched stiffly along his sides. The door was opened by the foreigner with the long black beard. No word was spoken. Mr Red raised his left hand and made some passes in the air. His bearded friend raised his left hand and imitated the passes with perfect solemnity. Mr Red crossed the threshold, turned, and solemnly beckoned to Dr O'Grady to follow him.

'I see,' said the doctor, in a cheerful, conversational tone, 'that you are all Freemasons here. It's an interesting profession. Or should I call it a religion? I'm not one myself. I always heard it involved a man in a lot of subscriptions to charities.'

Mr Red made no reply. He crossed the hall, flung open a door with a magnificent gesture, and motioned Dr O'Grady to enter the dining-room. The doctor hesitated for a moment. He was not a nervous man, but he was startled by what he saw. The room was brightly lit with four large lamps. The walls were hung with crimson cloth on which were embroidered curious beasts, something like crocodiles, but with much longer legs than crocodiles have, and with forked tongues. They were all bright yellow, and stood out vividly from their crimson background.

'Enter,' said Mr Red.

Dr O'Grady faced the crocodiles. In the course of his medical experience he had often met men who had seen such beasts in unlikely places and been haunted by them unpleasantly; but his own conscience was clear. He was strictly temperate, and he knew that the pictures on the walls in front of him could not be a symptom of delirium. Mr Red followed him into the room and shut the door. It was painted crimson on the inside, and a large yellow crocodile crawled across it.

'I suppose,' said Dr O'Grady, 'that you got leave from Lord Manton to paper and paint the house. I dare say this sort of thing'—he waved his hand towards the crocodile on the door, which was surrounded with a litter of repulsive young ones —'is the latest thing in art; but you'll excuse my saying that it's not precisely comfortable or soothing. I hope you don't intend to include one of those beasts in your new statue.'

Mr Red made no reply. He crossed the room, opened a cupboard, and took out of it a bottle and some glasses. He set them on the table and poured out some wine. Dr O'Grady, watching his movements, was inclined to revise the opinion that he had formed during the drive. He was majestic.

'Drink,' said Mr Red.

Dr O'Grady looked at the wine dubiously. It was bright

green. He was accustomed to purple, yellow, and even white beverages. He did not like the look of the stuff in the glass in front of him.

'If,' he said, 'that is the liqueur which the French drink, absinthe, or whatever they call it, I think I won't venture on a whole claret glass of it. I'm a temperate man, and I must keep my hand steady if I'm to spend the rest of the night picking grains of shot out of your friend.'

'Drink,' said Mr Red again.

Dr O'Grady felt that it was time to assert himself. He was a friendly, and good-tempered man, but he did not like being ordered about in monosyllables.

'Look here,' he said, 'I'm not a Freemason, or a Rosicrucian, or an Esoteric Buddhist, or the Grand Llama of Tibet, or anything of that kind. I don't deny that your manner may be all right with other sculptors, or with those who are initiated into your secrets, and I dare say you have to live up to this thing in order to produce really first-rate statues. But I'm an ordinary doctor and I'm not accustomed to it. If you have whisky or any other civilized drink, I don't mind taking a drop before I see the patient; but I'm not going to run the risk of intoxicating myself with some strange spirit. And what's more, I'm not going to be talked to as if you were a newly invented kind of automatic machine that can only utter one word at a time and won't say that unless a penny has been dropped into the slot.'

'Your fee,' said Mr Red, laying an envelope on the table.

Dr O'Grady took it up and opened it. It contained a ten-pound Bank of England note. His slight irritation passed away at once. Never before in the course of his career as a doctor had he received so large a fee. Then a sharp suspicion crossed his mind. A fee of such extravagant amount must be meant to purchase something else besides his medical skill. Men, even if they are as rich as Mr Red appeared to be, even if they have the eyes of a mad gander and an eccentric taste in house decoration, do not pay ten pounds to a country doctor for dressing a wound. Dr O'Grady began to wonder whether he might not be called upon to deal with the victim of some kind of foul play, whether he were being paid to keep his mouth shut.

'Follow me,' said Mr Red.

Dr O'Grady followed him out of the dining-room and up two flights of stairs. He made up his mind that his silence, supposing silence to be possible, was worth more than ten pounds. He determined to keep Mr Red's secret if it did not turn out to be a very gruesome one, but to make Mr Red pay handsomely. One hundred pounds was the amount he fixed on. That sum, divided between Mr Lorraine Vavasour and Jimmy O'Loughlin, would pacify them both for a time.

Mr Red stopped outside a bedroom door, and Dr O'Grady saw on it four large white letters, A.M.B.A. Mr Red opened the door. On a bed at the far end of the room lay the servant who used to drive into Clonmore and buy things at Jimmy O'Loughlin's shop. He was lying face downwards and groaning.

'Exert your skill as a physician,' said Mr Red, waving his hand in the direction of the bed.

'Don't you be a damneder ass than you can help,' said Dr O'Grady cheerfully.

He crossed the room and examined the man on the bed.

'Look here,' he said, turning to Mr Red, 'you told me that this man was suffering from the result of an accident he had had with a gun. Well, he isn't. I defy any man to scorch the skin off the backs of both his own legs with a gun. The thing simply couldn't be done.'

'Exert your skill as a physician, and be silent,' said Mr Red.

'You may fancy yourself to be the Cham of Tartary,' said Dr O'Grady, 'or Augustus Cæsar, or Napoleon Bonaparte, or a Field Marshal in the army of the Emperor of Abyssinia, but you've got to give some account of how that man flayed the backs of his legs or else I'll have the police in here to-morrow.'

28

Mr Red smiled, waved his hand loftily, and left the room.

Dr O'Grady, his professional instinct aroused, proceeded to dress the man's wounds. They were not dangerous, but they were extremely painful, and at first the doctor asked no questions. At length his curiosity became too strong for him.

'How did you get yourself into such a devil of a state?' he asked.

The man groaned.

'It looks to me,' said Dr O'Grady, 'as if you'd sat down in a bath of paraffin oil and then struck a match on the seat of your breeches. Was that how it happened?'

The man groaned again.

'If it wasn't that, ' said Dr O'Grady, 'you must have tied a string round your ankles, stuffed the legs of your trousers with boxes of matches, and then rubbed yourself against something until they went off. I can't imagine anything else that could have got you into the state that you're in.'

'I was smoking,' said the man at last, 'in the chamber of Research.'

'In the what?'

'It's what 'e calls it,' said the man. 'I don't know no other name for it.'

'Perhaps the floor of the Chamber of Research was covered with gunpowder behind where you were standing, and you dropped a lighted match into it.'

''Ow was I to know the stuff would go off?'

'If you knew it was gunpowder,' said Dr O'Grady, 'you might have guessed it would go off if you dropped a match into it.'

'It weren't gunpowder, not likely. It were some bloomin' stuff 'e made. 'E's always messing about making stuff, and none of it ever went off before.'

'If you mean Mr Red,' said Dr O'Grady, 'I can quite imagine that the stuff he made wouldn't go off. Unless, of course, it was intended not to. From what I've seen of him so far, I should say that his notion of manufacturing dynamite would be to take a hundredweight or so of toothpowder, and say to it, "Powder, explode." Still, you ought to have been more careful.'

''E's a damned ass,' said the man.

'He is,' said Dr O'Grady. 'Still, even an ass, if he goes on experimenting for four months in a chamber specially set apart for research, is sure to hit upon something that will explode by the end of the time. By the way, do you happen to know where he got that dining-room wall-paper with the crocodiles on it?'

The door opened and Mr Red stalked into the room.

'Follow me,' he said to Dr O'Grady.

'All right. I've finished with this fellow's legs for the present. I'll call again tomorrow afternoon, or rather, this afternoon. He'll get along all right. There's nothing to be frightened about. You may give him a little beef-tea and—— Damn it all! Augustus Cæsar has gone! Good-bye, my man; I'll see you again soon. I must hurry off now. It won't do to keep the Field Marshal waiting. The crocodiles might get on his nerves if he was left too long in the room alone with them.'

3

DR O'GRADY left the room and closed the door behind him. His spirits, owing to the ten-pound note which lay in his breast pocket, were cheerful. He whistled 'The Minstrel Boy' as he walked along the passage. Just as he reached that part of the tune which goes with the discovery of the boy in the ranks of death he stopped abruptly and swore. He was seized from behind by two men, flung to the ground with some violence, and held there flat on his back. A few useless struggles convinced him that he could not make good his escape. He lay still and looked at his captors. The foreign gentleman with the long black beard was one of them. The other was the man whom Dr O'Grady had declared to be a Norwegian. He was a powerful man, adorned with a mass of fair hair which fell down over his forehead and gave him a look of unkempt ferocity. Behind these two who knelt beside and on Dr O'Grady stood Mr Red.

'Hullo, Emperor!' said the Doctor, 'what's the game now? If you want a gladiatorial show, with me and these two swashbucklers as chief performers, you ought to have given me fair notice. You can't expect a man to put up much of a fight when he's caught from behind just as he's in the middle of whistling a tune.'

'You have learned too much,' said Mr Red, with fierce intensity. 'It is necessary in the interests of the Brotherhood to secure your silence.'

'Right,' said Dr O'Grady. 'You shall secure it. One hundred and fifty pounds down and the secrets of the Brotherhood are safe. Or if prompt cash inconveniences you in any way, I'll be quite content with your name on the back of a bill. Jimmy O'Loughlin would cash it.'

'I have passed judgment on you,' said Mr Red, 'and the scales are depressed on the side of mercy. Your life is spared. You remain a captive until the plans of the Brotherhood are matured and discovery can be set at defiance. Then you will be released.'

'If that's all,' said Dr O'Grady, 'you needn't have knocked me down and set these two brigands to kneel on my chest and legs. I haven't the slightest objection to remaining a captive. I shall enjoy it. Of course, I shall expect to be paid a reasonable fee for my time. I'm a professional man.'

'Number 2 and Number 3,' said Mr Red, 'will bind you and convey you to the place of confinement.'

He spoke a few words to his assistants in a language which Dr O'Grady did not understand. Two ropes were produced.

'If you choose to tie me up,' said Dr O'Grady, 'you can do it of course. But you'll simply be wasting time and energy. I've told you already that I don't in the least mind being a captive. Just you tell me the place you want me to go to, and if it isn't an insanitary, underground dungeon, I shall step into it with the greatest pleasure, and stay there without making the least attempt at escape as long as you choose to go on paying me my fees.'

'Give your parole,' said Mr Red.

'Parole? Oh yes, of course; I know the thing you mean now. I'll give it, certainly—swear it if you like. And now, like a good man, tell your fair-haired pirate to get off my legs. He's hurting my left ankle abominably.'

Mr Red gave an order, and Dr O'Grady was allowed to stand up.

'Now for the cell,' he said. 'I know this house pretty well, and I should suggest that you give me the two rooms on the top floor which open into each other. And look here, Emperor, I'm a first-class political prisoner, of course. I'm not going to do any hard labour, or get out of bed before I want to in the morning. I must be decently fed, and supplied with tobacco. You agree to all that I suppose?'

'Lead the prisoner upstairs,' said Mr Red.

'One minute,' said Dr O'Grady. 'We haven't settled yet about my fee. Let me see, what would you say—my time is valuable, you know. I have a very extensive practice, including the nobility and gentry of the neighbourhood; Lord Manton, for instance, and Jimmy O'Loughlin's wife. What would you say to——? Good Lord! Emperor, put that thing down, it might go off!'

Mr Red had taken a revolver from his pocket, and pointed it at Dr O'Grady's head.

'Lead the prisoner upstairs,' he said.

'I'm going all right,' said Dr O'Grady. 'But, like a good man, put down that pistol. I dare say it's not loaded, and I'm sure you don't mean to pull the trigger; but it makes me feel nervous. If you injure me you will be in a frightful fix. There isn't another doctor nearer than Ballymoy, and he's no good as a surgeon. Do be careful.'

Mr Red took no notice of this remonstrance. He held the revolver at arm's length, pointed straight at Dr O'Grady's head. The doctor turned quickly and walked upstairs. He was ushered into a large empty room, and bidden to stand in a corner of it. Still covered by the threatening revolver he watched various preparations made, first for his security, then for his comfort. There were two windows in the room. The black-bearded foreigner nailed barbed wire across them in such a way as to make an entanglement through which it was impossible to thrust even a hand.

'That's quite unnecessary,' said Dr O'Grady. 'I'm familiar with this house, have been over it half a dozen times with Lord Manton, and I know that there's a sheer drop of thirty feet out of those windows on the paved yard at the back of the house. I shouldn't dream of trying to jump out.'

Mr Red stood with the revolver in his hand glaring at Dr O'Grady. His two assistants left the room.

'I do wish,' said the doctor plaintively, 'that you'd put that gun down.'

By way of reply, Mr Red settled himself in an heroic attitude, something like that usually adopted by the hero on the cover of a sixpenny novel when he is defending his lady from desperate villains. He kept the revolver levelled at Dr O'Grady's head. The bearded man, Number 2, returned, dragging a small iron bedstead after him. Number 3 followed him with a mattress, pillows, and some blankets.

'For me?' said Dr O'Grady. 'Thanks. Now fetch a wash-hand-stand, a jug and basin, a table, a couple of chairs, some food, tobacco, and a few books. Then I'll be able to manage along all right.'

One thing after another was added to the furniture of the room until it began to look fairly comfortable. Dr O'Grady observed with satisfaction that a substantial meal was spread on the table, and a box of cigars laid on the washhand-stand.

'Would it be any harm my asking,' he said, 'how long you intend to keep me here? I have some rather pressing engagements just at present, and I should like to have an idea when I'll get home. Of course, I don't press the question if it inconveniences the Brotherhood to answer it before the plans are matured.'

'You shall be paid at the rate of £4 a day during the time that you are detained,' said Mr Red.

'Make it £5,' said Dr O'Grady, 'and I'll stay a year with you and settle my own washing bills.'

'In four weeks,' said Mr Red, 'the plans of the Brotherhood will be matured, and you can be released.'

'I'm sorry it's no longer,' said Dr O'Grady. 'The arrangement is perfectly satisfactory to me. But look here, Emperor, have you taken into consideration that I shall be missed? Before four weeks are out they'll be certain to start out looking for me. Search parties will go out with lanterns and bloodhounds. You know the kind of thing I mean. They won't come straight here, of course; nobody has any reason to suppose that I'm in this house; but sooner or later they certainly will come. I don't mind telling you that there are a couple of men—Jimmy O'Loughlin for one, and Lorraine Vavasour for another—who will be particularly keen on finding me. What will you do when they turn up?'

'The waters of the bay are deep,' said Mr Red grimly. 'Your body will not be found.'

'I catch your meaning all right,' said Dr O'Grady, 'but I think you'll make a mistake if you push things to extremes in that way. You've got the usual idea into your head that Ireland is a country in which every one kills any one they don't like, and no questions are ever asked. I don't in the least blame you for thinking so. Any intelligent man, reading the newspapers, would be forced to that conclusion; but, as a matter of fact, Ireland isn't that sort of country at all. We have our little differences with each other, of course; all high-spirited people quarrel now and then, but we really hardly ever drown anybody. We don't want to; but even if we were ever so keen we couldn't do so without great risk. The country is overrun with police, and—— I beg your pardon, did you speak?'

Mr Red had not actually spoken. He had snarled in a curious and vicious way.

'The police——' said Dr O'Grady.

Mr Red snarled again.

'If you object to my mentioning them by name,' said Dr O'Grady, 'I won't do it. All I wanted to say was that in Ireland they live extremely dull lives, and any little excite-ment—a cattle drive, or an escaped lunatic—is a positive god-send to them. A murder—perhaps I ought to say an informal execution, such as you contemplate—would bring them down to this neighbourhood in thousands. There'd be so many of them that they simply wouldn't be able to help tripping over my body wherever you hid it. Don't imagine that I'm saying all this with a view to preventing your cutting my throat. What I'm really thinking about, what you ought to be think-ing about, is the Brotherhood. How will its plans be matured if you get yourself hanged? And they will hang you, you know.'

'I am prepared to die,' said Mr Red majestically, 'in the cause of the Anti-Militarist Brotherhood of Anarchists.'

'Of course you are. Anybody who knows anything about military anarchists knows that. My point is that your life is too valuable to be thrown away. How would poor Long Beard get on? And the other fair-haired highwayman? Neither of them knows a word of English.'

'If the accursed minions of an effete tyranny seize me——!'

'Quite so. I see your point. Death before dishonour, and all that kind of thing. But why let it come to that? I am perfectly willing to stay here as long as you like at the liberal salary you offer, cash down every evening. I'm quite as anxious as you are to keep the accursed minions of the what-do-you-call-it away from Rosivera. I don't mind telling you in confidence that I have reasons of my own for avoiding any contact with the law at present. In my particular case it isn't nearly so effete as you appear to think it ought to be. But I needn't go into all that. It wouldn't interest you, and it's no pleasure to me to talk about that beast Lorraine Vavasour. What I want to suggest is a simple and practicable way of avoiding all fuss, and keeping the accursed minions quiet in their barracks.'

'Speak,' said Mr Red.

'I am speaking. For a man who hasn't had any breakfast this morning, I flatter myself that I'm speaking pretty fluently. Don't be captious, Field Marshal. I don't mind your manner a bit, now that I'm getting used to it. I know that it's quite the right kind of manner for a military anarchist, but there's no use over-doing it.'

'Your plan?' said Mr Red, fingering the revolver.

'I wish you'd lay that weapon down, Emperor. I've told you half a dozen times that I haven't the least intention of trying to escape, and it will be a horrid nuisance if the thing goes off and injures me. My suggestion is simply this. I'll write a letter blotted all over with tears, saying that driven to desperation by Lorraine Vavasour and Jimmy O'Loughlin I've committed suicide, and that all search for my body will be vain. Owing to circumstances which I need not explain, circumstances not unconnected with Lorraine Vavasour, the story will be believed in Clonmore and no further steps will be taken in the matter. All you will have to do is to drop the letter into the pillar-box which is only half a mile from your gate. I happen to know that that box is cleared at eight p.m., so any time today will do. I'll address it to the police sergeant.'

Mr Red gave an order to one of the two foreigners. The man

left the room and returned in a few minutes with a supply of note-paper, a pen, and a bottle of ink. He laid them beside the food on the table in the middle of the room.

'Write,' said Mr Red.

'I forgot to mention,' said Dr O'Grady, 'that I'm engaged to be married to a young lady in Leeds. Miss Blow is her name —Adeline Maud Blow. I dare say you've heard of her father in connection with cigars. He's a tobacconist and advertises a good deal. "Blow's beauties, twopence each". You must have heard of them. They're beastly things as a matter of fact, and I don't recommend them to friends, but they're amazingly popular.'

'Write,' said Mr Red.

'I am going to write. Don't hustle me, like a good man. What I want to say to you is this, that I must send a line to Adeline Maud as well as to the police sergeant. I want to tell her that I'm not really dead, only bluffing.'

'That,' said Mr Red, 'is impossible.'

'Nonsense. There's nothing impossible about it. It's just as easy to write two letters as one. I shan't mention the Brotherhood to her, and if I did she would have more sense than to talk about it. If you don't believe me you can read the letter yourself.'

'I trust no woman.'

'That,' said Dr O'Grady, 'is a most illiberal sentiment, and I'm surprised to hear you utter it. If you'd been an old-fashioned Tory now, or an Irish landlord, or a Liberal Cabinet Minister, I could have understood your position; but in a military——'

'Anti-militarist,' said Mr Red.

'That's what I meant. In an anti-militarist, that sort of prejudice against women is most inconsistent. Who was it that hammered a nail into Sisera's head? A woman, and an anti-military woman. Who was it that stuck a knife into that horrid beast Marat, when he was sitting in his bath? A woman again. Who was it that shot that Russian governor the

37

other day? I've forgotten his name for the minute, but you know who I mean. It was a woman. She did for him on a railway platform. And yet you stand up there calling yourself an advanced kind of anarchist, and say that you can't trust a woman. Emperor, you ought to be ashamed of yourself. Just think the matter out and you'll see that when it comes to thorough-going, out-and-out revolutions women are quite the most trustworthy kind of people there are.'

Mr Red gave another brief order in his foreign language. The fair-haired anarchist stepped forward and took away the note-paper, pen and ink.

'What are you at now?' said Dr O'Grady. 'Surely to goodness you're not going back on the suicide plan? Oh, very well. I can't help it. But you'll be sorry afterwards when the police come here looking for me.'

'I have spoken,' said Mr Red.

'You have not. You've growled occasionally, but nobody could call your remarks speaking.'

'I leave you,' said Mr Red. 'Remember.'

'Remember what? Oh, you're going, are you? Just wait one instant. You refuse to let me write to Adeline Maud. Very well. You don't know Adeline Maud, but I do. Even supposing the police can't find me, or my body after you've cut my throat, and supposing that Jimmy O'Loughlin and Lorraine Vavasour give up the pursuit—from what I know of Lorraine I think it most unlikely that he will—you'll still have to reckon with Adeline Maud. She's a most determined young woman. All the perseverance which has gone to making "Blow's beauties" the popular smokes they are at twopence each has descended from her father to her. When she finds out that I've disappeared she'll go on searching till she finds me. The ordinary sleuth-hound is absolutely nothing to her for persistence in the chase. It will be far wiser for you—in the interests of the Brotherhood I mean—to let me head her off, by telling her that I'll turn up again all right.'

'Farewell,' said Mr Red.

'I ought to mention before you go,' said Dr O'Grady, 'that Adeline Maud may be in Clonmore tomorrow. I'm expecting a visit—Damn it! The fool is gone and shut the door behind him.'

Mr Red had, in fact, entirely ignored the announcement of Miss Blow's impending arrival. He and his two friends left the room, and, distrustful of the parole which had been given, locked the door behind them. Dr O'Grady turned to the breakfast provided for him with an excellent appetite.

'Silly old ass that Emperor is,' he murmured. 'I suppose now he'll go and sit down beside his yellow crocodiles in the dining-room and try to invent some new kind of dynamite. He ought, as a matter of fact, to be in an asylum. Some day he will be if he doesn't blow himself up first. Anyhow this is a jolly good business for me. If he chooses to pay me four pounds a day for sitting here twiddling my thumbs, I'm quite content. I ony hope it will be some time before they think of looking for me at Rosivera. I must try and hit on a plan for putting the police off the scent. I wonder how long it will last. The Field Marshal suggested four weeks. Seven times four—even putting it as low as four pounds a day—and I'll try to screw him up a bit—seven times four are twenty-eight. And four times twenty-eight is a hundred and twelve. That with the tenner I've got will make £122. I'll make a clear £100 out of it anyway, and they won't have time to elect another dispensary doctor before I get out.'

4

Patsy Devlin strolled into the Imperial Hotel at noon. He found Jimmy O'Loughlin, the proprietor, behind the bar, and was served at once with a pint of porter.

'It's fine weather for the hay, thanks be to God,' he observed.

In Connacht the hay harvest is gathered during the month of August, and Patsy's comment on the weather was seasonable.

'I've seen worse,' said Jimmy O'Loughlin. 'But what's on you at all, Patsy, that you haven't been next or nigh the place this two months or more?'

'Be damn, but after the way you behaved over the election of the inspector of sheep dipping, the wonder is that I'd ever enter your door again. What would hinder you giving me the job as soon as another?'

Jimmy O'Loughlin did not wish to discuss the subject. He was, as a trader ought to be, a peaceable individual, anxious to live on good terms with all possible customers. He realized that the election was a subject on which Patsy was likely to feel bitterly. He filled another glass with porter from the tap and handed it silently across the counter. Patsy tendered a coin in payment.

'I'll not take it from you,' said Jimmy O'Loughlin heartily. 'It would be a queer thing if I wouldn't give you a sup at my own expense now that you are here after all this length of time. How's herself?'

Patsy Devlin took a pull at the second pint of porter.

'She's only middling. She was complaining these two days

of an impression on the chest and a sort of rumbling within in herself that wouldn't let her rest easy in her bed.'

'Do you tell me that? And did you fetch the doctor to her?'

'I did not then.'

'And why not?'

Patsy Devlin finished the porter and winked across the bar at Jimmy O'Loughlin. Jimmy failed to catch the meaning of the wink.

'If it was a red ticket you wanted,' he said, 'you know very well that you've nothing to do but ask me for it. But Dr O'Grady, the poor man, would go to you without that.'

'If I did be wanting a red ticket,' said Patsy, 'it wouldn't be you I'd ask for it. There's them would give it to me and maybe something along with it, and what's more, did give it to me no later than this morning.'

'Well,' said Jimmy, who guessed at the identity of the unnamed benefactor, 'and if so be that his lordship is after giving you the ticket, why didn't you go and fetch the doctor to herself?'

'I went for him right enough.'

'And do you mean to tell me that he refused to attend the call and you with the red ticket in your hand? For if he did——'

'He wasn't within when I went for him.'

The explanation was perfectly simple and natural; but Jimmy O'Loughlin, noting the manner in which it was given, realized there was something behind it.

'What do you mean?' he asked.

Patsy Devlin winked again, Jimmy, vaguely anxious, but not knowing what to fear, handed his visitor a third pint of porter.

'I'm thinking,' said Patsy, 'that it's about time for us to be making a move in the matter of collecting funds for the horse races and athletic sports. The season's going on and if we don't have them before the end of the month the days will be getting short on us. I suppose now I may put you down for a pound the same as last year?'

'You may,' said Jimmy. 'But what was it you were after telling me about Dr O'Grady?'

'Does he owe you any money?'

'He does, a power.'

'Then you'll not see it. Devil the penny of it ever you'll handle, no matter how you try.'

Patsy chuckled. He had nourished a grudge against Jimmy O'Loughlin ever since the election of the inspector of sheep dipping.

'And why will I not?'

'Because the doctor's gone, that's why. He's off to America, and every stick of furniture he owns is gone along with him.'

'He is not,' said Jimmy. 'He couldn't. It was only last night he passed this door, looking the same as usual. I was speaking to him myself, and him on his way home after being out beyond in the bog.'

'It was last night he went.'

'He couldn't. Sure you know as well as I do there's no train.'

'There's the goods that passes at one o'clock. What would hinder him getting into one of them cattle trucks? Who'd see him? Anyway, whether it was that way he went or another, he's gone. And you may be looking for your money from New York. Be damn, but I'd take half a crown for all of it you'll ever get.'

'I don't believe you,' said Jimmy; but it was evident that he was fighting desperately against conviction.

'Go round to the house then yourself and you'll see. He's not in it, and what's more he didn't leave it this morning, for old Biddy Halloran was watching out for him along the road the way he'd renew the bottle he gave her for the rheumatism, and if he'd gone out she'd have seen him.'

'It might be,' said Jimmy, 'that he was called out in the night and didn't get back yet.'

'It might; but it wasn't. I'm spending the morning since ten o'clock making inquiries here and there, and devil the one there is in the parish sick enough to be fetching the doctor out in the middle of the night. If there was I'd have heard of it. And Father Moroney would have heard of it, but he didn't, for I asked him this minute.'

'And what did he say?'

'He said very much what I'm saying myself, that the doctor's gone. "And small blame to him," says Father Moroney, "with the way that old reprobate of a Jimmy O'Loughlin, who's no better than a gombeen man, has him persecuted for the trifle of money he owes." It's the truth I'm telling you.'

It was not the truth, but it could scarcely be called a lie, for the essence of a lie is the desire to deceive, and Patsy Devlin invented the speech he put into the priest's mouth without the least hope of its being believed. The best he expected was to exasperate Jimmy O'Loughlin. Even in this he failed.

'If so be he's gone,' said Jimmy, 'and I wouldn't say but he might, I'd as soon he got clear off out of this as not. I'll lose upwards of thirty pounds by him, but I'd sooner lose it than see the doctor tormented by that bloodsucker of a fellow from Dublin that has a bill of his. I've a great liking for the doctor, and always had. He was an innocent poor man that wouldn't harm a child, besides being pleasant and agreeable as e'er a one you'd meet.'

Patsy Devlin felt aggrieved. He had sprung his mine on Jimmy O'Loughlin, and the wretched thing had somehow failed to explode. He had looked forward to enjoying a torrent of oaths and bitter speeches directed against the absconding debtor. He had hoped to see Jimmy writhe in impotent rage at the loss of his money.

'Be damn!' he said helplessly.

'And anyway,' said Jimmy O'Loughlin, 'there's the furniture of the house left, and it'll be a queer thing if I don't get

43

a hold of the best of it before ever the Dublin man—Vavasour or some such they call him—hears that the doctor's gone.'

There was no more spirit left in Patsy Devlin. He did not even repeat the obviously incredible statement that the doctor had secretly carried his furniture away with him in the middle of the night.

'The train's in,' he said, changing the subject abruptly, 'for I hear the cars coming down from the station. If so be now that there should be a traveller in belonging to one of them drapery firms, or Campbell's traveller with the flour, you might give me the word so as I can get a subscription out of him for the sports. The most use those fellows are is to subscribe to one thing or another where subscriptions is needed.'

Jimmy O'Loughlin nodded. He realized the importance of the commercial traveller as a contributor to local funds of every kind. He left the door and reached the bar of the hotel just as his bus, a ramshackle, dilapidated vehicle drawn by a sickly horse, drew up. It contained a lady. Jimmy O'Loughlin appraised her at a glance as she stepped out of the bus. She was dressed in a grey tweed coat and skirt of good cut and expensive appearance. She wore gloves which looked almost new, and she had an umbrella with a silver handle. She was tall and carried herself with the air of one who was accustomed to command service from those around her. Her way of walking reminded Jimmy O'Loughlin of Lady Flavia Canning, Lord Manton's daughter; but this lady was a great deal younger and better-looking than Lady Flavia. Jimmy O'Loughlin allowed his eyes to leave her for an instant and seek the roof of the bus. On it was a large travelling trunk, a handsome bag, and a bundle of rugs and golf clubs. Jimmy's decision was made in an instant. He addressed his guest as 'my lady'.

She made no protest against the title.

'Can I get a room in the hotel?' she asked.

'Certainly, my lady. Why not? Thomas, will you bring the lady's luggage in at once and take it up to number two, that's the front room on the first floor. Your ladyship will be wanting a private sitting-room?'

'If I do,' she said, 'I shall ask for it.'

Jimmy O'Loughlin was snubbed, but he bore no malice. A lady of title has a right to snub hotel-keepers. He stole a glance at the label on her luggage as Thomas, the driver of the bus, passed him with the trunk on his shoulders. He discovered that she was not a lady of title. 'Miss A. M. Blow,' he read. 'Passenger to Clonmore.' The name struck him as being familiar, but for a moment he could not recollect where he had heard it. Then he remembered. Miss Blow passed upstairs guided by Bridgy, the maid. Patsy Devlin emerged from the bar.

'It's the doctor's young lady,' whispered Jimmy O'Loughlin.

'Is it, be damn? How do you know that?'

'Didn't he often tell me,' said Jimmy, 'that he was to be married to a young lady out of Leeds or one of them towns beyond in England, and that her name was Miss Blow? And didn't I see it on her trunk, "Miss A. M. Blow"? Would there be two in the world of the name?'

'And what would bring her down to Clonmore?'

'How would I know? Unless maybe she's heard of the misfortunes that has the doctor pretty near beat. She might have seen his name in the paper when the judgment was gave against him.'

'She might: but if she did wouldn't she keep away from him as far as ever she could?'

'She would not,' said Jimmy O'Loughlin. 'That's not the sort she is. I seen her and you didn't.'

'I did.'

'Well, and if you did you might have known that she'd be the sort that would come down after him the minute she got word of the trouble that was on him. Believe you me, Patsy Devlin, that's a fine girl.'

'She's a good-looking one anyway,' said Patsy, 'but mighty proud, I'd say.'

'You may say that. I'd sooner she married the doctor than me, and that's the truth.'

'What'll she do now,' said Patsy, 'when she finds that the doctor's gone and left her?'

'It'll be best,' said Jimmy, 'if we keep it from her.'

'How can you keep it from her when the man's gone? Won't she be asking to see him?'

'There's ways of doing things. What would you say now if I was to tell her that the doctor had gone off on a holiday for six weeks with the permission of the Board of Guardians and that there'd have to be a substitute appointed in his place? Would she be contented with that, do you think?'

'She might,' said Patsy, 'but she might not. She'd be wanting his address anyway.'

'If she wanted it, it would be mighty hard to keep it from the like of that one.'

'You haven't got it to give, and so you can't give it,' said Patsy.

Miss Blow came downstairs as he spoke and walked up to Jimmy O'Loughlin.

'Will you kindly have some luncheon ready for me,' she said, 'at two o'clock?'

'Certainly, miss, why not? Is there any particular thing that your ladyship would fancy, such as a chop or the like?'

He reverted to the 'ladyship' again, although he knew her name and degree. The girl's manner seemed to force him to. She deserved something better than a mere 'miss'.

'In the meanwhile will you be so good as to tell me where Dr O'Grady lives?'

'Is it Dr O'Grady? Well now, never a nicer gentleman there is about the place, nor one that's more thought of, or better liked than Dr O'Grady. It's him that does be taking his dinner up at the Castle with the old lord and attending to his duties to the poor the same as if he was one of themselves. Many's the time I've said to him: "Dr O'Grady," says I, "if anything was to take you away out of Clonmore,

46

and I don't deny but what you ought to be in a less backward place, but if ever——"'

'Will you be so good as to tell me where he lives?' said Miss Blow.

Patsy Devlin interposed at this point of the conversation with an air of contempt for Jimmy O'Loughlin.

'Can't you stop your talking,' he said, 'and tell the lady where the doctor lives?'

Jimmy cast a venomous glance at him.

'I will tell your ladyship to be sure. Why not? But it will be of no use for you to go and call on him today. Patsy Devlin here is after telling me this minute that he's not at home.'

Miss Blow turned to Patsy.

'Do you know,' she asked, 'when he's likely to be back?'

'I do not know, my lady. But I'd say it wouldn't be for a couple of days anyway.'

'A couple of days! Where has he gone to?'

'It's what Mr O'Loughlin there was just after telling me, your ladyship, and he's the Chairman of the Board of Guardians, that the doctor did ask for leave to go on a holiday. But I wouldn't say that he'd be away for very long.'

'When did he ask for a holiday?' said Miss Blow to Jimmy O'Loughlin.

'It was Patsy Devlin told me,' said Jimmy; 'and six weeks was the time he mentioned.'

Miss Blow turned again to Patsy Devlin; but he had vanished. Having committed Jimmy O'Loughlin, as Chairman of the Board of Guardians, to the fact of the doctor's holiday, he slipped quietly into the bar.

'I don't believe,' said Miss Blow, 'that you're telling me the truth.'

'He was not,' said Jimmy, sacrificing his friend with the utmost promptitude. 'It's seldom he does that same. Devil the bigger liar, begging your ladyship's pardon for the word, devil the bigger liar there is in Connacht than that same Patsy

Devlin, and it's what everyone that knows him would tell you.'

'I don't,' said Miss Blow severely, 'see very much to choose between you and him.'

In England people have a great regard for the truth so long as it does not interfere with business. Miss Blow expressed her scorn for the two men who had tried to deceive her quite plainly both by her words and the tone in which she spoke them. In Connacht truth is less respected. Good manners and consideration for other people's feelings are looked upon as virtues superior to blunt accuracy of statement. Jimmy O'Loughlin lied feebly, but he lied with the best intentions. He wanted to spare Miss Blow the knowledge that her lover had deserted her. In return she insulted him; but even under the sting of her words he recollected that courtesy is due to every lady, especially to one as good-looking as Miss Blow. It was not until she had turned her back on him and left the hotel that he murmured under his breath—

'May the Lord help the poor doctor if it ever comes to his being married by the like of her.'

5

MISS BLOW came back for her luncheon, and then, asking no more help or advice from Jimmy O'Loughlin, went out and made her way to Dr O'Grady's house. It stood a few hundred yards from the village in the middle of a small field. Miss Blow knocked and rang at the door, though she had

48

no real expectation of its being opened to her. She walked round the house and peered in at the windows. The rooms on the ground floor showed every sign of having been recently occupied by a person of untidy habits. She reached the yard, surveyed the coach house and the stable which had once sheltered a good horse. She tried the kitchen door and found it bolted against her. The kitchen had a disused and neglected appearance which puzzled her. She returned to the front of the house and sat down on a stone to think out the position in which she found herself.

Patsy Devlin, who had followed her from the hotel, watched her proceedings from a distance with great interest. He afterwards made a report to Jimmy O'Loughlin, a masterly report which interpreted her actions, and added a picturesque touch at the end. Patsy Devlin would have written good histories if fortune had made him a university professor instead of a blacksmith.

'You'd have been sorry for the creature,' he said, 'if you'd seen her sitting there on a lump of a stone with the tears running down the two cheeks of her the same as if you were after beating her with a stick.'

'I am sorry for her,' said Jimmy. It's herself has her own share of trouble before her when she finds out that the doctor's off to America without so much as leaving word for her to go after him.'

It did not seem likely that Miss Blow would easily arrive at a knowledge of the full extent of her misery. Biddy Halloran, the rheumatic old lady who had waited long on the roadside for the doctor in the morning, was still lurking near the house when Miss Blow reached it. She, like Patsy Devlin, watched the examination of the premises with deep interest. When Miss Blow sat down on the stone, Biddy Halloran hobbled up to her.

'Is it the doctor you're looking for?' she said. 'For if it is, it's hardly ever you'll see him again.'

Miss Blow was startled, and demanded an explanation of

49

the words. Biddy, who was slightly deaf, pretended to be very deaf indeed. Miss Blow's clear voice and determination of manner subdued her in the end. She professed to be the only person in Clonmore who really knew what had happened to the doctor.

'Holidays, is it?' she said, recollecting what Patsy Devlin had told her, 'No, nor work either. It's to Dublin he has gone, and it's little pleasure he'll find there. Och, but he was a fine man and it's a pity of him!'

'Tell me at once,' said Miss Blow, 'what he went to Dublin to do.'

'There was a lump in the inside of him,' said Biddy, 'a gathering like; and many's the time he told me of that same. It was the size of a young pullet's egg, and you'd feel it lepping when you put your hand on it, the same as it might be a trout. "Biddy, agra," he says, speaking to me, as it might be to yourself or to some other young lady that would be in it, instead of an old woman like myself, "medicine's no good," says he, "but the knife is what's wanted." "Would you not be afeard," I said, "to be trusting yourself to them murdering doctors up in Dublin, and maybe a young lady somewhere that would be crying her eyes out after you, and you dead?" "I would not be afeared," says he—och, but he was a fine man!—"only I wouldn't like the girl that's to be married to me to know," says he; "I'd be obliged to you if you'd keep it from her," says he; "and what's more, I'll go tomorrow."'

Miss Blow did not believe a word of it, but old Biddy Halloran reaped her reward. Jimmy O'Loughlin, when the conversation was reported to him, sent her a present of a bottle of patent medicine which had been a long time in the shop and appeared to be unsaleable. It professed to cure indigestion, and to free the system from uric acid if taken in teaspoonsful after meals. Biddy Halloran rubbed it into her knees and felt her rheumatic pains greatly relieved.

Miss Blow sought and, after many inquiries, found the woman who had acted as Dr O'Grady's housekeeper, and had

50

basely deserted him in the hour of his extremest need. She had taken refuge, as a temporary lodger, with Patsy Devlin's wife. It was understood that she would pay for her board and lodging when her solicitor succeeded in recovering the wages due to her. The news of the doctor's flight had greatly depressed her. She felt that she was greatly wronged; but even when smarting from her loss, she was not so heartless as to revenge herself by telling the terrible truth to an innocent and beautiful creature like Miss Blow. She gave it as her opinion that the doctor, driven to desperation, perhaps almost starved, had poisoned himself. He had, she asserted, bottles enough in his surgery to poison the whole country. His body, she believed, was lying in the house behind the locked doors.

'If so be,' she added, 'that the rats haven't him ate; for the like of that house with rats, I never seen. Many's the time, when the doctor would be out, I've sat the whole evening on the kitchen table, with my legs tucked under me, and them running across the floor the same as hens would come to you when you'd be calling them. You couldn't put down a dish out of your hand, but they'd whip the bit off it before your eyes, without you'd have some sort of a cover to put over it.'

No one who was even slightly acquainted with Dr O'Grady could suppose him capable of suicide under any conceivable circumstances. Miss Blow, who of course knew him well, was quite unimpressed by the housekeeper's horrible suggestion. But she realized that the truth, whatever it was, was not to be reached by inquiries. Jimmy O'Loughlin and Patsy Devlin lied to her. So did Biddy Halloran. So did the housekeeper. There was evidently an organised conspiracy among the people of Clonmore for the concealment of the truth. Miss Blow had a logical mind. It seemed plain to her that if everybody agreed to tell her lies the truth must be something of a dangerous or uncomfortable kind. She had some knowledge of Ireland, gleaned from the leading articles of English newspapers. She knew, for instance, that it was a country of secret societies, of midnight murders, of defeated justice, of lawlessness which scorned the cloak of hypocrisy. She had heard of reigns of terror, emphasised by the epithet 'veritable'. She was firmly convinced that the lives of respectable people were not safe on the west side of the Shannon. Her father, Mr Blow of the cigars, was an earnest politician, and at election times his house was full of literature about Ireland which his his daughter read. Her experience of the people of Clonmore went far beyond her worst expectations. She made up her mind that Dr O'Grady had been murdered; that everybody in the place knew the fact; and that, either through fear or an innate fondness for crime, no one would help to bring the murderers to justice.

It is very much to her credit that she did not take the next train home; for she must have thought that her own life was in great danger. But she was a young woman of determination and courage. She made up her mind to discover and bring to the scaffold the men who had done away with Dr O'Grady. Her suspicions fastened, in the first instance, on Jimmy O'Loughlin and Patsy Devlin.

'Mr O'Loughlin,' she said, when she returned to the hotel after her interview with the housekeeper, 'kindly tell me who is the nearest magistrate.'

'You haven't far to go to look for a magistrate, miss, if that's all you want. I'm one myself.'

'I don't believe you,' said Miss Blow, rudely.

'Maybe not,' said Jimmy; 'but I'm telling you the truth for all that. Let you go into the Petty Sessions Court tomorrow, and see if I'm not sitting there on the bench; with the police and Mr Goddard himself, that's the officer, if he happens to be over from Ballymoy, doing what I bid them, be that same agreeable to them or not; and oftener it's not, for them police think a lot of themselves. When you see me there administering the law you'll be sorry for what you're after saying. It's the Chairman of the Urban District Council I am, and an ex-officio magistrate, thanks be to God.'

'Is there any other magistrate in the neighbourhood?'

'There is not; for the R. M. lives away off at Ballymoy, and that's better than twelve miles from this. There's ne'er another, only myself and Lord Manton up at the Castle, and he never sits on the bench from one year's end to another, unless maybe there's a job on that he would like to have his finger in.'

The title produced its effect on Miss Blow. Earls are much less common in the industrial districts of England than they are in Ireland. The statistics have never been exactly worked out, but there can be little doubt that there are far more earls to every thousand common men in Ireland than in any other part of the three kingdoms. This is not because governments are more generous to the Irish in the matter of titles. The explanation is to be found in the fact that untitled people in Ireland tend to disappear, thinned out by famine, emigration, and various diseases, while the earls survive. In England it is the noblemen who die away, being, as every reader of popular English novels knows, a degraded set of men, addicted to frightful vices, whereas the working men and the great middle class increase rapidly, their morality being of a very superior kind. Curiously enough, the English, though perfectly aware of the facts, respect their debauched earls greatly, on account, it may be supposed, of their rarity. The Irish, on the other hand, think very little of an earl, regard him as in many respects similar to an ordinary man; earls being, as has been said, comparatively common in Ireland. Miss Blow, who had never to her knowledge seen an earl, brightened up at the mention of Lord Manton.

'I'll go up to the Castle,' she said, 'and see him tomorrow morning.'

Jimmy O'Loughlin sent a message to Patsy Devlin, asking him to call at the hotel that evening. The fact that he had not been elected inspector of sheep dipping still rankled in Patsy's mind. He blamed Jimmy O'Loughlin more than anyone else for his rejection. He made up his mind to obey the summons, but not to be seduced from the path of righteous wrath by

53

porter or whisky. He would refuse contemptuously to oblige Jimmy in any way.

He was received in Jimmy O'Loughlin's private office, a small room at the back of the hotel, which looked out on the yard. The walls were adorned with two pictures, enlarged photographs of eminent ecclesiastics with small eyes and puffy cheeks. The table was mahogany and was covered with circular stains of various sizes. There was a sideboard with a very dilapidated cruet-stand and two teapots on it. The chairs were all rickety. A writing-desk, which stood under the window, was littered with a number of exceedingly dirty papers. On the table in the middle of the room, by way of preparation for Patsy's visit, were arranged a jug of porter, a bottle of whisky, a water croft, and several tumblers.

'Fill your glass,' said Jimmy hospitably, 'and light your pipe. You can start on the porter, and finish up with the spirits.'

Patsy poured out the porter suspiciously, and drank a tumbler full without any signs of appreciation.

'There isn't one about the place,' said Jimmy, 'that's better acquainted with the old earl up at the Castle than yourself. He thinks a deal of you, and well he may.'

'He gave me a letter,' said Patsy, 'at the time of the election. But it's little heed you or the rest of them paid to it.'

Jimmy was anxious to avoid the subject of the election.

'I'm told,' he said, 'that whatever you might ask of him, he'd do.'

Patsy was susceptible to flattery of this kind.

'He always thought a deal of me and my father before me,' he said. 'You could tell the opinion he had of me by the letter he wrote. And why wouldn't he when either my father or myself put the shoes on every horse that's come and gone from the Castle this fifty years.'

'I could tell what he thought of you,' said Jimmy. 'Sure anybody could.'

'You could tell it, if so be you read the letter.'

'The doctor's young lady,' said Jimmy, 'is going up to see the earl tomorrow. The Lord save her, but she's half distracted with grief this minute.'

'And what good will going to the Castle do her? Sure he doesn't know where the doctor is no more than another.'

'He might tell her the truth,' said Jimmy.

'Be damn, but he might, not knowing.'

'And if he did, the girl's heart would be broke.'

'It would surely.'

'We've kept it from her,' said Jimmy, 'and may the Lord forgive us for the lies we're after telling, fresh ones every hour of the day. And if so be that now, at the latter end, she hears how the doctor has gone and left her it'll go through her terrible, worse than the influenza.'

'And what would you consider would be the best to be done?' asked Patsy.

'I was thinking that maybe, if you was to see him tomorrow, early, before ever she gets at him with her questions, and if you were to give him the word, that it might be, coming from a man like yourself that he has a respect for, that he'd hold off from telling her.'

'He might.'

'And will you do it, Patsy Devlin? Will you do it for the sake of the fine young girl that's upstairs, this minute, heart scalded with the sorrow that's on her?'

'It's little you deserve the like from me,' said Patsy, 'you nor the rest of the Guardians. But I'll do it for the sake of the girl.'

'I knew you would,' said Jimmy. 'It's a good heart you have in you, Patsy Devlin, and a feeling for them that's in distress. But the porter's finished. Will I draw you another jug of the same, or will you try the whisky for a change?'

Patsy indicated the whisky bottle with his thumb. He remained lost in deep thought while the cork was drawn and a considerable quantity of the spirit poured into the tumbler before him. Indeed, so complete was his abstraction that the glass might have been absolutely filled with undiluted whisky if Jimmy had not, of his own accord, stayed the flow of it.'

'I'm collecting the town and the neighbourhood,' said Patsy, 'for the sports, and there's no reason that I can see why I shouldn't call on his lordship tomorrow and ask for a subscription.'

'You might.'

'And in the course of conversation I could draw down upon the doctor and the young lady and give him the word.'

'Take care now would she be beforehand with you, if so being you were a bit late in going.'

'Let you see to that,' said Patsy.

'I might try,' said Jimmy: 'but she's that headstrong and determined it's hard to stop her once she takes the notion into her head.'

'Be damn!' said Patsy, 'but however you manage you'll have to stop her. The old earl doesn't have his breakfast took till near ten o'clock, and if I was to try and see him before half-past ten, he'd eat the face off me.'

'I'll do the best I can,' said Jimmy. 'I'll tell Bridgy to have the breakfast late on her. She does be wanting it at half-past eight.'

'Let her want. If she gets it by half-past nine itself oughtn't she to be content? There's many a house where she wouldn't get it then.'

'Content or not,' said Jimmy heroically, 'it's at half-past nine she'll have it tomorrow anyway.'

'And after that,' said Patsy, 'it could be that the horse might be lame the way she'd have to walk.'

'It could.'

'And if you sent her round by the big gate,' said Patsy, 'it would put a couple of miles on her beyond what she'd have to walk if she was to go up through the deer park.'

'It would,' said Jimmy; 'but the talk she'll give after will be terrible to listen to.'

'Don't tell me. A young lady like her wouldn't know how to curse.'

'It's not cursing,' said Jimmy, 'but it's a way she has of speaking that would make you feel as if the rats beyond in the haggard was Christians compared to you.'

'Let her talk.'

'And she looks at you straight in the face,' said Jimmy, 'the same as if she was trying to see what would be in the inside of your head, and feeling middling sure all the time that there wasn't much in it, beyond the sweepings of the street.'

'It's for her own good you're doing it,' said Patsy.

There was some consolation in the thought. But Patsy, even while making the suggestion, felt that a good conscience is not always a sufficient support in well-doing.

'You might,' he added, 'be out about the place and let herself talk to her till the worst of it was over.'

This plan, which perhaps would not have suited Mrs O'Loughlin, commended itself to Jimmy; but it did not make himself altogether comfortable about the future.

'I might,' he said, 'and I will, but she'll get me for sure at the latter end.'

If he had done as his conscience suggested, Patsy Devlin would have gone home at once after settling Miss Blow's business for her. But the whisky bottle was still more than half full, and it seemed a pity to break up a pleasant party at an early hour. He started a fresh subject of conversation, one that he hoped would be interesting to his host.

'Tell me this now,' he said. 'Do you think that fellow down at Rosivera, the same that brought the pianos along with him, would give a subscription to the sports?'

'I don't know,' said Jimmy. 'He's queer. I never set eyes upon him myself since I finished carting the packing-cases down to Rosivera.'

'They tell me that he does be calling at your shop for his bread and the like, and leaving a power of money with you.'

'I wouldn't say he left so much at all,' said Jimmy cautiously.

57

'And anyway it's a servant that did be coming every day till today, and then it was some sort of a foreigner with a written order, him not being able to speak English.'

'Would you see your way to asking him for a subscription?'

'How would I do it, when he can't know a word I say to him, nor him to me? Why won't you talk sense?'

'And where's the man himself, and the fellow that did speak English?'

'How would I know? If it's a subscription you want from him, you'd better go over to Rosivera and ask for it.'

'They say,' said Patsy thoughtfully, 'that he has plenty to give. A man like that with a motor car running on the road every day, and two foreign gentlemen, let alone an Englishman, to wait on him, must have a power of money. I wouldn't wonder now, if I took him the right way, but he'd give five pounds. I might drop him a hint that five pounds is the least that any of the gentry would give to the sports.'

'Let you see what you can get out of him,' said Jimmy, 'and the more the better.'

Jimmy had got all he wanted out of Patsy Devlin. He did not care very much whether Mr Red subscribed to the sports or not. He took the whisky bottle and drove the cork home into its neck with a blow of his fist. Patsy looked regretfully at it, but he was a man of self-respect. He would neither ask for, nor hint that he wanted, a drink which his host did not seem inclined to offer him freely. He realized what the decisive blow given to the cork meant. There would be no more whisky for him unless he chose to go out to the bar and pay for it there in the usual way. This he was unwilling to do. Later on in the month, when the collection for the sports was complete, he might be in a position to spend lavishly; but for the present he felt it necessary to economize.

'I'll be off with me,' he said. 'It'll be best, seeing I have to be up at the Castle early tomorrow. Later on in the day I might be going over to Rosivera to see what's to be got out of the man that's there. If he's as rich as you're after telling me

he'll never miss a pound, or for the matter of that five pound.
I'll have a try at him anyway.'

6

'Is there any news of the doctor?' asked Lord Manton.

He was standing on the steps outside the door of Clonmore
Castle. He had just given Patsy Devlin a sovereign for the
Horse Races and Athletic Sports, and was endeavouring to
cut short the thanks with which the subscription was received.

'There is not, your lordship, devil the word; and why would
there? It could be that he's on the sea by this time, and, anyway, why should he be wanting to tell us where he is? Isn't it
enough of their persecuting he had without going out of his
way to ask for more?'

Lord Manton, like everybody else, regarded Dr O'Grady's
flight to America as the natural result of his financial embarrassment. He was sorry; but he recognized that the doctor
had taken the wisest course.

'Might I be speaking a word to your lordship about the
doctor?'

'Certainly, Patsy.'

'It's what Jimmy O'Loughlin was saying to me that there'd
be no need, if your lordship was agreeable to the same, to be
telling the young lady the way the doctor is gone off and left
her without a word. She has trouble enough, the creature,
without that.'

'What young lady?'

'Be damn!' said Patsy hurriedly, 'if there isn't herself coming up the avenue. It wouldn't do for her to see me talking to your lordship. I'd better be going before she's on top of us.'

Patsy Devlin slipped round the corner of the Castle, and dodging through a plantation of laurels, made his way to the stable-yard. Lord Manton was left to watch the approach of Miss Blow, without any very clear idea of what she was likely to want of him; or how Jimmy O'Loughlin and Patsy Devlin expected to keep the doctor's flight a secret from her. He observed with pleasure that she was more than commonly good-looking, that she carried herself well, and wore clothes which set off a fine figure. He had heard from Dr O'Grady of the daughter of the Leeds tobacconist, and had formed a mental picture of her which in no way corresponded to the young lady who approached him. He reflected that she was probably in deep distress, and he looked forward with some pleasure to an interview in the course of which she was almost certain to cry. He had no objection to playing the part of comforter to a charming girl. His face expressed fatherly benignity when Miss Blow reached him.

'Am I addressing Lord Manton?' she asked.

'Certainly. Is there anything I can do for you?'

He almost added the words 'my dear', but there was a look in Miss Blow's fine eyes which checked him. He decided that paternal affection would come in more appropriately after she began to cry.

'I am Miss Blow,' she said.

'Come in,' said Lord Manton, 'come in. You must be tired after your walk. Let me lead the way into the library. I have often heard of you from my friend Dr O'Grady, and if there is anything I can do to help you I shall be most happy to do it.'

He set Miss Blow in a deep chair near the window, pulled over another chair for himself, and sat down beside her.

'I am entirely at your service,' he said. 'It will be a pleasure

to me to give any help in my power to a charming young lady.
I——'

Miss Blow's eyes warned him again. There was a hard
glitter in them very little suggestive of tears. He stopped
abruptly.

'I understand that you are a magistrate,' she said.

Lord Manton bowed. Then he sat up straight in his chair
and tried to express in his attitude a proper judicial solemnity.

'I want,' said Miss Blow, 'to have Dr O'Grady found at
once.'

'A very natural and a very proper wish,' said Lord Manton. 'I am in entire sympathy with you. I should like very
much to find Dr O'Grady. But——'

'Dead or alive,' said Miss Blow firmly.

'My dear Miss Blow!' The 'my dear' came quite naturally
to his lips this time. The words expressed sheer astonishment.
There was no suggestion of affection, paternal or other, in the
way he uttered them.

'Dead or alive,' said Miss Blow again.

'Don't make such horrible suggestions, Miss Blow. I assure
you there's not the slightest reason for supposing that Dr
O'Grady is anything but alive and well.'

'Then where is he?' Miss Blow spoke sharply, incisively.
Lord Manton began to think that she must be some new kind
of girl, quite outside of his experience, one who felt more
indignation than sorrow at the loss of her lover.

'I understand,' he said, 'that he is absent from home, temporarily absent. I have no doubt——'

Miss Blow rose from her chair and took up her umbrella.

'You're like all the rest,' she said. 'You are as bad as the
hotel-keeper and his friend. You are simply trying to put me
off with lies. Good morning.'

'Wait a moment. Please do not hurry away. I am not like all
the rest, really. I assure you I'm—compared to Patsy Devlin,
for instance,—I'm a miserably inefficient liar. Please sit down
again.'

Miss Blow allowed herself to be persuaded.

'Tell me the truth,' she said; 'and then find his body.'

'The truth,' said Lord Manton, 'is painful—very painful. But it's not so bad as that. Dr. O'Grady has been for some time past in a position of considerable pecuniary embarrassment.'

'He was up to his neck in debt,' said Miss Blow bluntly. 'I know that. That's what brought me here. And now I find he's gone.'

There was just a hint of a break in her voice as she spoke the last words. Lord Manton thought that tears were at last imminent. He felt more at his ease, and ventured to take her hand in his and to stroke it gently. She snatched it from him.

'You're worse than the others,' she said. 'How dare you?'

For a moment Lord Manton thought that she was going to box his ears. He drew away from her hurriedly and attempted an apology.

'I am sincerely sorry,' he said. 'For the moment I forgot that you were not my daughter. She always came to me with her troubles ever since she was quite a child. I got into the way of taking her hand——'

'Never mind about my hand. Tell me the truth about Dr O'Grady.'

Lord Manton saw that she was mollified. To be mistaken for the daughter of an earl is a soothing thing under any circumstances. He thought for an instant of trying to repossess himself of her hand; but Miss Blow's eyes, though no longer passionate, were steely. He felt himself aggrieved, and spoke with brutal directness.

'To put the matter plainly,' he said, 'Dr O'Grady has run away from his creditors.'

'I don't believe a word of it,' said Miss Blow.

'I have no doubt that he intended to let you know where he was going. I expect he wants you to go after him and join him there—make a fresh start, you know, in the New World, and build up a happy home, where the miserable past may be forgotten. That's what he means. I'm convinced of it. Only

62

he had to leave this rather hurriedly in the middle of the night. But don't be despondent, Miss Blow; you'll get a letter from him soon.'

'That's all nonsense,' said Miss Blow. 'He's done nothing of the sort.'

'But, my dear young lady, how can you possibly speak so confidently? He's not the first man who has run away under such circumstances. Plenty of people do it. I assure you. It's not even considered disgraceful.'

'I know he didn't.'

'But how do you know?'

'Because I wrote to him a week ago, when I first heard he was in trouble, and told him I was coming over here to see him. I said that father would help him out of his difficulties, whatever they were. Do you think that, after that, he'd run away and not so much as tell me where he was going?'

Lord Manton did not know what to think. Dr O'Grady had disappeared. There was no getting out of that. It was a patent fact. On the other hand, if Mr Blow had really offered to pay the doctor's debts, there seemed to be no reason why he should disappear. No doubt the wealthy proprietor of the well-known twopenny Beauties could afford to pay Mr Lorraine Vavasour's bill twenty times over if necessary. Still, Dr O'Grady had disappeared.

'You are all,' said Miss Blow passionately, 'a lot of slanderous busy-bodies, telling lies and meddling with everybody's business because you have no business of your own to attend to. My poor Lucius has been murdered among you, and now not one of you will help me to get at the truth; but I'll do it in spite of you.'

Lord Manton looked at her. She was undeniably handsome: handsomer than ever now that she was in a rage. It occurred to him suddenly that Dr O'Grady might have a reason for disappearing, quite unconnected with the money he owed. He was engaged to be married to Miss Blow. It was possible that the idea of home life with this masterful and passionate young woman for a partner might be rather terrifying. Besides, the wife who pays her husband's debts for him has a hold over him ever afterwards; and Miss Blow seemed exactly the kind of lady who would take advantage of such a position. She would certainly make him aware of the fact. Lord Manton thought he understood at last why Dr O'Grady had run away. Miss Blow's face was buried in her handkerchief. She was not crying, but she was flushed after her outburst, and preferred to keep her face covered. Lord Manton ventured on a smile and a gentle chuckle.

'I assure you,' he said soothingly, 'that he hasn't been murdered. Who would murder him? Everybody in the neighbourhood was fond of him. I don't think there was a man, woman, or child but loved him. I did myself.'

'If you loved him,' said Miss Blow, 'show it now.'

'I will, with pleasure; but how?'

'Give me a search warrant.'

'A search warrant! But——'

'Yes, a search warrant; and I will insist upon the police executing it.'

'I haven't the least doubt you will; but—but what do you mean to search?'

'Every house in the neighbourhood. Every house until I find him.'

'But he isn't in a house. Do try to be reasonable, Miss Blow. Even if he's murdered—and I'm quite sure he's not—he wouldn't be in a house. His body would be hidden in a wood or a bog-hole or a river, or wherever it is that murderers usually do hide bodies.'

'You admit then that he has been murdered.'

'No, I don't. You mustn't catch up my words like that. All I said was that, if he had been murdered, he wouldn't be living in a house, and so a search warrant wouldn't be any use to you. You don't really want a warrant at all. You don't even want the police. All you have to do is to go prowling round the country, poking into any shadowy-looking hole you see with the point of your umbrella until you come across his body.'

The interview was beginning to tire Lord Manton. He was not accustomed to being bullied by handsome girls, and he did not like it.

'Perhaps you'd like to start at once,' he said politely.

'It's impossible,' she said, 'for me to search the country by myself.'

'Not at all. Nothing is impossible for a young lady of your energy. Start with the wood behind this house; it's very thick in parts, quite a likely spot for a corpse; and come in here for lunch when you've finished.'

'Give me a written order to the police,' said Miss Blow, 'commanding them to aid me in my search.'

'It wouldn't be the least use to you, I assure you. You've no idea what independent people the police are. An order from me would simply put their backs up and make them determined not to help you.'

'Give me the order, and I'll see that they execute it.'

'My dear Miss Blow, I can't, I really can't. Try the Chief Secretary. You'll find him in his office at Dublin Castle. He's a most agreeable man. You needn't be the least bit afraid of him. Not that it's likely you would be. He's much more likely to be afraid of you. It won't take you long. You can run up by the night mail and——'

'Give me the order.'

Lord Manton surrendered. He crossed the room, sat down at his desk, and wrote—

'Sergeant Farrelly, R.I.C. Kindly give all the assistance in your power to Miss Blow, the bearer of this note, who wishes to search the country for a dead body.—MANTON.'

'If that is any use to you,' he said, 'you're welcome to it. Let me know how you get on. Any time you happen to find yourself near this house, drop in for luncheon or tea. Good-bye.'

Miss Blow rose, bowed, and left the room. Lord Manton rang the bell.

'Wilkins,' he said to his butler.

'Yes, my lord.'

'You saw that young lady who left the house just now? Very well, if she calls again, and I happen to be out, you are to give her breakfast, luncheon, tea or dinner according to the hour of the day. If I happen to be at home you are to stay in the room during the time she is with me, as a chaperone. You understand, Wilkins?'

'Yes, my lord.'

'She doesn't require a chaperone, but I do. I don't feel safe when I'm alone with her. And Wilkins, if she brings a corpse along with her, either Dr O'Grady's corpse or any other, you will provide proper accommodation for it. Put it on the table in the servants' hall with a sheet over it, and send out to the garden for flowers—white flowers.'

'Yes, my lord.'

'One thing more, Wilkins; if Sergeant Farrelly or any policeman comes up here from the barracks either today or tomorrow and asks to see me, tell him I'm out, and that it won't be the least use his waiting because I won't be in before midnight and probably not then.'

'Yes, my lord.'

Wilkins left the room, and Lord Manton, taking the chair in which Miss Blow had been sitting, lit a cigarette. There was a stealthy step on the gravel outside. He looked up and saw Patsy Devlin's face pressed against the window. He rose, opened the window, and asked Patsy what he wanted.

'Might I be so bold as to put a question to your lordship?'

'Is it about Miss Blow or Dr O'Grady?'

'It is,' said Patsy. 'It's about the both of them.'

'Out with it, then. That young woman and her relations with the doctor form quite the most interesting subject I know at present.'

'Did your lordship keep the truth from her?'

'I did my best not to, Patsy; but I think I may safely say that I did.'

Patsy pondered this saying. The meaning was not immediately obvious to him.

'It's what Jimmy O'Loughlin was saying to me last night,' he said, 'that if so be she heard that the doctor had left her, the creature's heart would be broke, and her as handsome a young girl as any you'd see.'

'At the present moment,' said Lord Manton, 'she believes that you and Jimmy O'Loughlin have murdered the doctor and concealed his body in a bog hole.'

'The Lord save us and deliver us! Was there ne'er another story you could tell her only that? Sure the police will be out after us.'

'She went straight from this house to the barracks,' said Lord Manton, 'and I shouldn't wonder if you were arrested before night.'

'Be damn!' said Patsy, 'saving your lordship's presence; but they couldn't take me for the like of that. There isn't one in the country but knows that I wouldn't lay a hand on the doctor, drunk or sober, not if it was to save my soul.'

'Don't you be too sure,' said Lord Manton. 'My own belief is that if Miss Blow doesn't come across the doctor in the course of the next twenty-four hours, she'll have you hanged for murdering him.'

'It's joking you are. She couldn't do it.'

'I am not joking. I defy any man to joke after spending half an hour with Miss Blow. She is the most determined young woman I ever met. She could do anything, absolutely anything. There isn't a judge or a jury could stand out against her for an hour. If I were you, Patsy, I'd make a bolt for it and join the doctor in America. Your life's not safe in this country. I expect by this time you have as much collected for the sports as would pay your passage out.'

'I have,' said Patsy; 'but I'll not go. I'll stand my trial, if it comes to that, sooner than have people saying it of me that I ever laid a hand on the doctor.'

'It's all very fine talking that way, but you won't feel at all so confident when you see the judge putting on the black cap; and a little later on, when the rope's round your neck, you'll be sorry you didn't take my advice. The thing for you to do is to skip while you've time. It'll take Miss Blow a good while to persuade the police to arrest you, but she'll do it in the end.'

7

A POET, writing, as some of them will, a parody on the work of another poet, has these words—

> 'To every Irishman on earth
> Arrest comes soon or late.'

Patsy Devlin did not read much poetry, and had never come across the lines. If he had met them, he would have recognized at once that they express a great truth. His experience of life convinced him that the law in Ireland, though erratic in its methods, may be relied on in the end to get the upper hand of either daring or innocence. The proceedings of the police, depending as they do on the view which some complete stranger has promised his constituents in England to take of Irish affairs, are quite incalculable. Patsy himself had been praised by political orators, had been favourably mentioned by eminent statesmen in the House of Commons itself, for actions which he would have kept concealed if he could. What seemed to him to be serious misdemeanours, if not actual crimes, had more than once turned out to be virtuous deeds. It seemed likely, therefore, that the law might occasionally regard entire innocence as highly culpable. He would have been indignant, but he would not have been greatly surprised, if the Government, that remote deity from which there is no appeal, had decreed his arrest, trial, and execution for the murder of Dr O'Grady. Patsy reasoned the matter out with himself. If, he thought, a man is not punished for the crimes he does commit, it is probable that he will be punished for those he has avoided committing. This consideration, coming on top of Lord Manton's friendly warning, made him uneasy. He determined to keep clear of the police barrack when he left Clonmore Castle.

Rosivera is a remote and lonely spot. It was extremely improbable that there would be any police lurking near it. It was not the sort of place to which a police sergeant would think of going if he were bent on the arrest of a murderous blacksmith. Patsy felt that he might, without running any undue risk, venture on a visit to Mr Red. He was not willing to forgo the chance of getting an additional subscription to the sports fund. He had in his pocket money enough to take him to America, but another pound, two pounds, perhaps even five pounds, would be very welcome to him. He was a good man, with a tender heart and a strong sense of his duty to those dependent on him. He wanted to be in a position to make some provision for the support of his wife and family when he left them. Mr Red's subscription, if Mr Red turned out to be a generous man, would enable him to leave Mrs Devlin and the children comfortably provided for.

He went to Rosivera by a circuitous route, avoiding the public roads as much as possible, walking over fields and finally along the sea-shore. When he came in sight of the house, he reconnoitred it carefully, and approached it very much as a skilful scout might advance on an enemy's camp, availing himself of all the cover which the country afforded. Satisfied at last that there was no police patrol in the neighbourhood, he made a circuit of the house, and finally reached the yard gate by way of the kitchen garden. He entered the yard and made sure that there was no one in it. He peeped into the stable and the cow-house and found that they were both empty. He opened the door of the coach-house and took a long look at the motor car which stood there. It was well cleaned; its lamps and other metalwork shone brilliantly; it was a very handsome vehicle. Patsy felt reassured. Mr Red might be eccentric, as Jimmy O'Loughlin hinted, might even be vicious, but he was unquestionably opulent. No one but a rich man could keep such a motor car. Patsy closed the coach-house door quietly and took a long look at the back windows of the house. They were all shut and veiled with drawn blinds; all of them, except one small window in the top storey. It was wide open. Patsy stared at it.

Suddenly, something flew from the window and dropped at Patsy's feet. It was a pellet of paper. Patsy looked round him curiously and then stooped and picked it up. He unwrapped the paper and discovered that it contained a small piece of china, apparently a fragment of a broken saucer. He put this into his waistcoat pocket and examined the paper in which it had been wrapped. He discovered a few words on it scribbled in pencil—

'Come back into the yard in twenty minutes. Don't wait now.—O'Grady.'

'Be damn,' said Patsy softly, 'it's the doctor himself!'

Being a man of high intelligence, with a natural taste for conspiracy, he acted in the wisest possible way. Without the smallest display of emotion, or a single glance at the window from which the communication had come, he turned and slouched carelessly towards the yard gate. It was flung open before he reached it, and Mr Red, a revolver in his hand, strode forward. Patsy displayed great presence of mind and resource.

'I'm just after knocking at the back door, your honour,' he

said, 'thinking that it might be more agreeable if I didn't go round to the front, where maybe you'd be entertaining company. It was that I was collecting a trifle from the gentry round about for the grand annual horseraces and athletic sports that does be held every year up beyond in Jimmy O'Loughlin's big field. And the committee would feel pleased, your honour, if you'd act as a vice-president or a starter, or the like, along with Lord Manton from the Castle.'

Mr Red raised the revolver and pointed it at Patsy's head.

'Hand me that note,' he said.

'Sure your honour's joking. What would a poor man like me be doing with a note? If you're the gentleman they say you are, it's yourself will be giving a note to me, and maybe a five-pound note for the sports.'

Mr Red took four steps forward, and stood so that Patsy had every opportunity of looking into the barrel of the revolver.

'Right about turn,' he said; 'march!'

'I was in the militia one time,' said Patsy, 'and I know well what you're saying. If it's into the house you want me to go through the back door, I'm willing. But there's no need for you to be looking at me that way or to be reaching out at me with your pistol. If you think I'm here trying to steal a motor car on you, you're making a big mistake. Anybody can tell you that I wouldn't do the like. If I wanted to itself I wouldn't be able. I couldn't drive one of them things no more than fly.'

'March!' said Mr Red.

He held the revolver within a couple of inches of Patsy's head.

'A gentleman like yourself,' said Patsy, 'likes his bit of a joke. I know well it's only funning you are and that it's not loaded; but I'd be obliged to you if you'd point it the other way. Them things goes off sometimes when you're not expecting them.'

By way of demonstrating that it was loaded, and that he was not 'funning', Mr Red fired a shot. The bullet went quite close to Patsy's head and buried itself in the kitchen door. Patsy, convinced that he had to do with a dangerous lunatic, turned quickly and walked into the kitchen. From the kitchen he was forced, at the point of the revolver, up several flights of stairs. He was bidden to halt at last opposite a door. Mr Red produced the key from his pocket, and, still keeping the revolver levelled at Patsy, opened the door.

'Enter,' he said.

'Be damn, but I will, and I'll be all the better pleased if you'll stay outside yourself.'

This was exactly what Mr Red did. The door was locked again, and Patsy found himself face to face with Dr O'Grady.

'I'm sorry,' said the doctor; 'I'm infernally sorry. I was an ass to throw you out that note. I might have known that the Field Marshal would be spying round somewhere. It's just the kind of absolutely idiotic thing he does rather well.'

'You needn't be sorry at all. Now that I know I'm not shot, I'd as soon be here as anywhere else.'

'Would you? I'm glad you're satisfied. All the same I wish you were out of it. Now that there are two of us here, the police are bound to come after us and find us.'

'They're out after me, anyway,' said Patsy. 'That's why I say I'd as soon be here as anywhere else.'

'And what do they want you for? Is it any of your League work?'

'It is not. It's nothing to do with the League, good or bad. It's for murdering you and concealing your body after.'

'Can't you talk sense, Patsy Devlin?'

'It's the truth I'm telling you, and I couldn't say different if I was put on my oath this minute.'

'But, damn it all, I'm not murdered; I'm alive.'

'That may be,' said Patsy. 'All I know is that Lord Manton's after telling the young lady that you are murdered; and what's more, he said it was Jimmy O'Loughlin and myself that done it.'

'Tell me the truth now, Patsy. Is Miss Blow in Clonmore?'

'She is.'

'You're sure of that?'

'I am sure. She came the day after you went to America. Why wouldn't I be sure when she has the whole of us riz ever since with the questions she did be asking about you; and not one in the place but told her lies, be the same more or less, for fear the creature would break her heart if she heard what you were after doing. And at the latter end his lordship told her we had murdered you, to quiet her like, for fear she might hear that you had gone to America, leaving her behind you, without ever a word to her, good nor bad.'

'Good God, man! But I haven't gone to America.'

'I see that well enough now. But tell me this, doctor, why didn't you send us word, so as we'd know what to say to her?'

'I couldn't. The first chance I got was when I dropped that note out of the window to you. If you'd come back to the yard the way I told you, I'd have had a letter written to Jimmy O'Loughlin that you could have taken back with you. I'd have explained the whole situation.'

'I was meaning to come back just as you bid me. Wasn't I walking out of the yard quiet and easy, so as I'd be able to come back at the end of half an hour or thereabouts, when that murdering villain came at me with a pistol and went very near shooting me dead?'

'I'll tell you what it is, Patsy. The sooner you're out of this the better. There's not the least difficulty about escaping. The Field Marshal thinks he's a tremendous swell at conspiracies of all sorts; but as a matter of fact he's a perfect fool, and I have the lock loosened on the door this minute. You can walk out any time you like; and the best time in my opinion will be tonight.'

'And why wouldn't you go yourself, doctor, if it's as easy as all that?'

'I don't want to go,' said the doctor. 'I'm very well contented where I am. It's much better for you to go.'

'How would it do if the both of us went?'

'It wouldn't do at all. I tell you I want to stay. I don't want to escape. But you must. I don't want the police here searching for me.'

'Be damn, then, but I won't go either! As sure as ever I went they'd have me hanged for murdering you, and that wouldn't suit me at all.'

'Don't be a fool, Patsy. How can they hang you for murdering me when I'm alive?'

'But—but—without I'd bring them here to see you they'd never believe that you weren't dead. What with the young lady going round the country cursing like mad at them that killed you, and the old lord telling the police it was me and Jimmy O'Loughlin done it, what chance would a poor man like myself have against them? They'd have me hanged, I'm telling you.'

'I'll give you two notes,' said Dr O'Grady; 'one to Lord Manton, and one to Jimmy O'Loughlin, and between the three of you it'll be a queer thing if you can't keep the police quiet and stop all this silly rot about my being murdered.'

'Will you give me a writing to the young lady herself?'

'I will not. I know very well what she'd do if she heard I was here. She'd come straight down after me.'

'I'm not saying but what she might. From what I see of her I'd say she's just the sort of a young lady that would.'

'Well, then, can't you understand that the last thing in the world I want is for her to know where I am? If I could have got a note to her at the first go off, before she came to Clonmore, it would have been all right. I'd have told her that I was detained here in attendance on an important case, and that she was to stay at home and not come near Clonmore till I sent her word. But that silly old ass of a Field Marshal thought he knew better than I did how to deal with a girl, and he wouldn't let me send the note. Then you and Jimmy O'Loughlin and Lord Manton, and I suppose every soul about the place, go stuffing her up with a pack of lies until——'

'Be damn, doctor, but that's a hard word. What we did was

74

for the best. You wouldn't have us tell the creature the truth, and her thinking all the time that you'd rather die than desert her?'

'Tell her the truth! What truth?'

'That you were off to America so as you wouldn't have to pay Jimmy O'Loughlin what you owed him.'

'But—oh, damn it all, Patsy, what a fool you are! That's not the truth. Can't you see that it's not the truth? Will I be obliged to leave a mark on your ugly face with my fist to prove to you that I'm not in America?'

'It was all the truth we had for her, anyway. But we wouldn't tell her. And why not? Because she was a fine girl, and we didn't want to see her going off into a decline before our eyes and maybe dying on us. And because we had a respect for your memory; and that's more than you had for yourself, hiding away here from a girl that any man might be proud to own. And it's more than you have for us, putting the hard word on us, and we doing the best we could from the start.'

Dr O'Grady was a reasonable man. His anger cooled. He came to see that his friends had acted with the best intentions. He apologized handsomely to Patsy Devlin.

'All the same,' he added, 'you will have to go. I tell you what it is, if the police do come here, the Field Marshal will shoot the two of us. He told me himself that that's what he'd do. And, whatever else he may be, he's a man of his word.'

'He dursn't, not with the police in the house. He'd be hanged.'

'He doesn't care a pin whether he's hanged or not. As a matter of fact, I expect he'd rather like to be hanged. He's an anti-militarist.'

'I was just thinking,' said Patsy, 'when he gave the word of command to me there in the yard, that he'd been in the militia himself some time.'

'Well, he hasn't, so you're out there. So far as I can make out, one of his main objects in life is to blow up the militia,

75

and the regular army along with it. He's an anarchist of the most advanced kind.'

'Be damn, and is he that?'

'He is. And I can tell you an anarchist isn't what you'd call a playboy. Anarchism isn't a bit like your futile old League. It doesn't go about the country making speeches and pretending it's going to boycott people that it hasn't the least notion of doing any harm to. A genuine anarchist, a man like the Field Marshal, for instance, doesn't say a word to anybody, but just goes quietly and blows up a town.'

'I'll not have you speaking against the League, doctor. I've been a member of it since ever there was a branch started in Clonmore. I'd be a member of it still, if it wasn't that they went against me the time of the election of the inspector of sheep dipping. I can tell you there's them in it would think very little of making the country hot for the man that went against the will of the people in the matter of grazing ranches or the like.'

'I don't want to argue about the League either on one side or another. What I'm trying to get you to understand is simply this. You've got to go, and to go tonight, as soon as ever the Field Marshal is tucked up in his little bed and the house quiet. Listen to me now, and I'll make the position plain to you. As long as I was here by myself I was more or less safe. The disappearance of one man doesn't make much difference in a neighbourhood like ours; but when it comes to two men vanishing in the inside of one week there's bound to be a fuss. The police will take the matter up to a certainty. If they come here—and they will come here when they've tried everywhere else—you and I will be shot by the Field Marshal.'

He looked at Patsy as he spoke, and noticed with regret that he was producing little or no impression.

'And what's more, I'll lose well over a hundred pounds; a hundred pounds that I want badly.'

'Why didn't you tell me that before?' said Patsy.

'Is it likely now that I'd want to stand between you and a

lump of money like that? I wouldn't do it to any man, much less one like yourself, that I have a respect for. Give me the writings now that we were speaking of, and I'll start at once.'

'You can't start till night; but I'll write the notes at once if you like.'

'And the one to the young lady along with the other two.'

'I told you before,' said Dr O'Grady, 'that I won't give you a note to her.'

'Then I'll stay where I am. It's more than I dare to go back without a line of some sort to quiet her. Don't I tell you she'd have me hanged? And when that's done she'll be down here after you with the police, and you'll be as badly off as you were before.'

'She'll not be able to do that. Lord Manton would stop the police.'

'She'll come without them, then. That sort of a young lady would do anything.'

'If she does,' said Dr O'Grady, 'the Field Marshal will shut her up too. He won't do her any harm, and I'll be delighted to have her here.'

'You want her here along with you?'

'I'd be glad to have her, of course. Don't you know that she and I are engaged to be married?'

'Well, aren't you the queer man? Anybody'd think you were trying to hide yourself from her for fear she'd marry you against your will.'

'Is that one of the lies you and Jimmy O'Loughlin have been telling Miss Blow?'

'It is not, of course.'

'Well, don't let me catch you saying anything of the sort, or it'll be the worse for you. Now, leave me in peace till I write the notes.'

'I'm not going with them,' said Patsy; 'so you needn't trouble yourself to be writing.'

'All right. If you prefer to stay here and be shot, you can. You'll be sorry afterwards, that's all. I tell you the Emperor is not a man to be trifled with. There's a fellow downstairs here that's sick, and I go twice every day to attend him. I give you my word, Patsy, all the time I'm dressing his wounds I have the muzzle of that revolver stuck up against the back of my neck. I'd be uncommonly nervous if I didn't know that the poor old Emperor is a good sort and reliable, in spite of his fondness for yellow crocodiles.'

'Is there crocodiles in this house?'

'There are; large yellow ones. The dining-room is crawling with them.'

'That settles it, then,' said Patsy. 'If I was ever so keen to get out of this, I wouldn't do it after that. I'd be in dread of them beasts; and I dursn't face them. They'd be out after me, and me going down the stairs in the dark; and I wouldn't know how to speak to them the way they wouldn't bite.'

'Don't be an ass, Patsy. They're not real crocodiles. They're dead.'

'Alive or dead, I'll not face them; so it's no use your talking. They're not what I'm used to, and I'd rather stay here along with you where I'd be safe.'

8

Miss Blow went straight from Clonmore Castle to the police barrack. She was received at the door by Constable Moriarty, who happened to be on duty at the time. He was a young man who had only recently joined the force. Miss Blow, after a glance at his smooth boyish face, asked to see the sergeant.

She was shown into a small room, known as the office, and kept waiting while Sergeant Farrelly, who was digging potatoes in the garden, 'cleaned himself'. Her manner, when he joined her, was peremptory. She demanded that a search party should start at once and scour the country for Dr O'Grady's body. Sergeant Farrelly was puzzled, and scratched his head. Miss Blow handed him Lord Manton's note. He read it, was very perplexed, and scratched his head again. Miss Blow pressed her demand.

'It will be better,' said the sergeant at last, 'if I go up to the Castle, and speak to his lordship myself. If you'll have the kindness, miss, to leave your name and address, I'll communicate with you.'

'I'll wait here,' said Miss Blow, 'till you return.'

'Is it in the barrack, miss?'

'Here,' said Miss Blow firmly.

Sergeant Farrelly looked at her helplessly. He did not want a handsome young lady in the barrack; he thought his office an unsuitable place for Miss Blow; but he saw no way of altering her determination. He left her and summoned Constable Moriarty.

'The young lady within,' he said, 'will wait in the office until such time as I come back from the Castle, where I'll be speaking on business to his lordship. I leave it to you, Constable Moriarty, to see that she's treated with proper respect.'

'Is it me?' said Moriarty.

'It is you. You can take her in yesterday's paper, and if it happens that she's read it already, you can talk to her, making yourself as pleasant and agreeable as you know how.'

Wilkins, Lord Manton's butler, was a good servant. He opened the door to Sergeant Farrelly at about twelve o'clock, and blandly gave the message with which he had been charged.

'His lordship is out, and it is uncertain at what hour he will return.'

Sergeant Farrelly was baffled. He went back to the barrack.

He found that Miss Blow had moved from the office, which was small and incommodious, and had settled herself in the men's day room. Constable Moriarty, embarrassed and very pink about the face, stood in front of her. Constable Cole, who was off duty, was grinning in a corner. Miss Blow at once reiterated her demand that a party should go out to look for Dr O'Grady's body. Sergeant Farrelly reasoned with her. When reason failed, he tried to impress her with the majesty of the law. He was a portly man and over six feet in height. On patrol duty, on guard over a public-house on Sunday or giving evidence in court as to the amount of drink taken by a prisoner, he was an impressive man. He did not impress Miss Blow. Being an English woman, she held the curious theory that the police exist for the protection of the public, and that they ought to engage willingly in the investigation of crime. Sergeant Farrelly knew, of course, that this was not true; but he was unable to explain his position to Miss Blow, because she would not listen to what he said.

At two o'clock, Miss Blow being still immovable in the day room of the barrack, Sergeant Farrelly started again for Clonmore Castle. This time he was accompanied by Constable Moriarty, who, reckless of the consequences of not obeying orders, refused to be left to entertain Miss Blow. Constable Cole slipped quietly out into the garden and took a turn at the potatoes which the sergeant had been obliged to leave undug.

Wilkins said politely what he had said before. Sergeant Farrelly and Moriarty sat down in the hall to wait. They waited till four o'clock. Then they returned to the barrack, hoping that Miss Blow would have gone home. They found that she had not gone and showed no signs of going. She was sitting in the men's room, eating biscuits out of a paper bag. It appeared afterwards that Constable Cole had gone out and bought the biscuits for her, fearing that she might be hungry. Sergeant Farrelly reprimanded him sharply for this.

Miss Blow gave the sergeant and his men her opinion of the Royal Irish Constabulary. She used plain and forcible language, repeating such words as incapacity, inefficiency, and cowardice at frequent intervals. She spoke for nearly half an hour, and then demanded again that the whole force should set out at once and search for Dr O'Grady's body. Constable Cole grinned and was caught in the act. The sergeant snubbed him promptly. Miss Blow took off her hat and jacket, and said she intended to stay where she was until a search party went out.

Sergeant Farrelly and his men withdrew and held a counsel in the kitchen. Constable Moriarty suggested that Miss Blow should be arrested on a charge of drunkenness, and locked up for the night.

'If she isn't drunk,' he argued, 'she wouldn't be behaving the way she is.'

His advice was not taken. In the first place, she was a well-dressed and good-looking young woman; and Sergeant Farrelly, being unmarried, was a courteous man. In the second place, she had come to the barrack bearing a note from Lord Manton, and however unintelligible the note might be, it had unquestionably been written by a peer of the realm. In the third place, as Constable Cole pointed out, their object was not to keep Miss Blow in the barrack, but to get her out. Pressed by Moriarty and the sergeant for an alternative scheme, Cole suggested vaguely that they should resort to what he called a 'stratagem'. This sounded well; but it turned out in the end that he had nothing better to suggest than that Jimmy O'Loughlin should be induced to send a message to her to the effect that her dinner was ready and would be spoiled if she kept it waiting. The plan received no support. Sergeant Farrelly pointed out that it would be most unwise to confess their difficulty to Jimmy O'Loughlin.

'That fellow,' he said, 'would take a delight in turning the police into ridicule, and setting the whole country laughing at us. And besides,' he said, with a look of withering contempt at Constable Cole, 'it's not likely she would be caring about her dinner after you giving her sixpennyworth of biscuits and more. Believe you me, she wouldn't mind this minute if she never saw dinner again.'

Half an hour later Sergeant Farrelly himself offered Miss Blow a cup of tea. He was a kindly man, as most police sergeants are, and it grieved him to think that the young lady who had established herself in his barrack was spending a whole day with nothing to eat except dry biscuits. She took the tea without thanks, and again demanded that the search for Dr O'Grady should begin. Sergeant Farrelly became desperate. He set out once again for Clonmore Castle. This time he was accompanied by both constables, and Miss Blow was left in sole possession of the barrack. He learned that Lord Manton was still out. After a short consultation, he and the two constables sat down in the hall to wait. They waited till ten o'clock, and would have waited longer still had not Wilkins informed them that it was his duty at that hour to lock up the house for the night. The police returned to their barrack, disputing hotly about the best way of disposing of Miss Blow for the night. To their immense relief they found that she had gone.

At nine o'clock next morning she walked into the barrack again and took her seat in the men's day room. This time she had with her a brown paper parcel. Constable Cole gave it as opinion that it contained provisions for the day.

'I shall stay here,' she said firmly, 'until you choose to do your duty.'

Sergeant Farrelly, who was refreshed and invigorated by his night's sleep, began to argue with her. The two constables stood near the door of the room and admired him. Miss Blow, adopting a particularly irritating kind of tactics, refused to pay any attention to his remarks. Whenever he paused to give her an opportunity of stating her case, she said—

'I shall sit here until you choose to do your duty.'

She had just repeated her formula for the ninth time when a groom rode up to the door of the barrack. He brought a note from Lord Manton.

'Sergeant Farrelly, R.I.C. Lord Manton is seriously annoyed to hear that the police spent the greater part of yesterday afternoon and evening in the hall of Clonmore Castle. Lord Lord Manton has not asked for police protection, and knows no reason why it should be forced on him. Lord Manton will not be at home today, and he requests that any communication by way of apology or explanation be made to him in writing.'

The note was passed round and read with dismay. Sergeant Farrell and the two constables, moved by a common impulse, withdrew together to the kitchen. For a time they stood silent and dejected. Then the sergeant, assuming an air of confident authority, gave his order.

'Constable Moriarty,' he said, 'you will take that note over to Ballymoy and hand it to the District Inspector. You will kindly explain at the same time the way we find ourselves fixed here.'

'Maybe,' said Moriarty, 'it would be as well if I was to take the other note along with it—the one his lordship was after sending with the young lady about the corpse of Dr O'Grady.'

'It would be as well,' said the sergeant; 'I'd be glad he'd see that note too. But it's the young lady has it and not me. Did you happen to think now of e'er a way that it could be got from her?'

'Would you ask her for it?' said Constable Moriarty.

'I might ask her for it, and I might ask the King if he'd lend me the loan of his crown to go courting in. I'd be as likely to get the one as the other by asking. If you can think of no better way of getting it than that, Constable Moriarty, you may go and ask for it yourself; and you can come back here and let us have a look at you, when she smacks your face.'

'We might try a stratagem with her,' said Constable Cole, who had made a similar suggestion the day before. 'I was reading a book one time about a man that was great on stratagems. There wasn't a thing would happen but he'd——I'm sorry now I haven't the book by me.'

'Stratagems be damned,' said Sergeant Farrelly. 'What

stratagem would you be proposing to try? Maybe you'd like me to send for Jimmy O'Loughlin and him to tell the young lady that his wife was wanting the note the way she could use it for lighting the kitchen fire to boil the kettle for tea. Is that your stratagem? Tell me now.'

'It is not,' said Constable Cole, with dignity, 'nor it isn't like it. If I was the sergeant here, I'd go to the young lady and I'd tell her, speaking civil and pleasant, that the District Inspector beyond in Ballymoy had sent a man over for the note, so as he could set the police all over looking for Dr O'Grady, and that he wouldn't be able to do that same without he got the note, on account of the way the law does be at the present time.'

'Is that what you call a stratagem?' said the sergeant. 'It's a lie I'd call it myself, a whole pack of lies, and it's just what they might take the stripes off me for saying, if so be I was fool enough to say it. Is it looking to be sergeant yourself in the place of me you are, that you'd suggest the like of that?'

'All stratagems is lies,' said Constable Cole soothingly. 'The one I'm suggesting is no worse than another.'

'Go and try her with it yourself, then,' said the sergeant, 'and see what you'll get out of it.'

Constable Cole, pursued by the sniggering laugh of Moriarty, left the kitchen and went into the day room. Miss Blow had made herself quite at home. On the iron-legged table with which the police barrack was provided lay her hat, her jacket, and her gloves. She was knitting a silk tie, meant perhaps as a present for her father, perhaps as an adornment for the corpse of Dr O'Grady when she found it. Constable Cole drew himself up stiffly to attention and addressed her—

'I beg your pardon, miss, but Sergeant Farrelly will be obliged to you if you'll lend him the loan of the note that Lord Manton gave you. He's thinking of sending a man over to Ballymoy to the D.I.'

'What's a D.I.?' asked Miss Blow.

84

'He's an officer, miss, a gentleman by the name of Mr Goddard.'

'Is he your superior officer?'

'He is, miss.'

'Then I'll go and see him myself, and take the note with me.'

The reply was quite unexpected. Constable Cole hesitated.

'It's better than twelve miles of a drive,' he said, 'and the road's none too good. And it could be, miss, that the D.I. might be off somewhere, shooting or the like, when you get there, and then you wouldn't find him.'

'If he is out, I shall wait for him.'

'I wouldn't doubt you, miss; but it could be——'

'No, it couldn't,' said Miss Blow. 'At all events, it won't. Kindly go and get the car at once.'

Constable Cole returned to the kitchen grinning broadly.

'It's yourself that's in luck this day, Moriarty,' he said. 'It's not every man that gets the chance of driving round the country on a car with the like of that one. Be careful now what you're saying to her, or you'll have the doctor out after you with a stick if he has to come all the way back from America for the purpose.'

'What do you mean?' said Moriarty.

'She said she'd go with you to Ballymoy, as soon as ever she heard it was you that was going. But if I hear tell of any impropriety of conduct, I'll send word to the red-haired girl that you used to be walking out with on Sundays when you were up in the depôt learning your drill. I heard of you.'

Moriarty was young, very young. He blushed hotly.

'I'd be ashamed of my life to be seen with her,' he said. 'I'd never hear the last of it.'

'Off with you at once and get the car,' said the sergeant. 'In the name of God, if the girl's willing to go out of this, will you take her along with you before she changes her mind? Haven't we had enough of her this two days?'

In less than half an hour the car—Jimmy O'Loughlin's car

85

—was at the door of the barrack. Constable Moriarty, in full panoply, his grey cape rolled round his chest, his carbine between his knees, sat on one side. Miss Blow, looking very handsome, got up on the other. Sergeant Farrelly wrapped a rug round her knees and tucked the end of it under her feet. Then he presented her with a sixpenny box of chocolates. He had gone round to Jimmy O'Loughlin's shop and bought this offering while the horse was being harnessed.

'It's a long drive you have before you,' he said, 'and I was thinking maybe you'd like something to comfort you on the way. It's no more than a trifle, and not what you'd be accustomed to, but Clonmore is a backward place, and it's the most thing of the kind there was in Jimmy O'Loughlin's shop.'

Constable Cole rushed from the barrack bare-headed, just as the car was starting. He had Miss Blow's brown paper parcel in his hand.

'You've forgotten your lunch, miss,' he shouted. 'You'll be wanting it before you're back.'

He stowed the parcel in the well of the car, and was able as he did so to still further embarrass the unfortunate Constable Moriarty.

'By rights,' he whispered, 'you ought to be sitting on the same side with her. It's what she'd expect of you; and if you don't do it when you get off to walk up Ballyglunin Hill, she'll be in a mighty bad temper against you have her safe with the D.I. If you're half a man, Moriarty, you'll do it.'

There was a good deal of excitement in the town when Miss Blow drove off under the escort of Constable Moriarty. The news that Jimmy O'Loughlin's car had been ordered for her and the constable spread so rapidly that by the time the start was actually made a small crowd had gathered in the street to see it. Afterwards, for more than an hour, men stopped casually at the barrack door, chatted on indifferent subjects with Sergeant Farrelly and Constable Cole, and then asked one or two leading questions about Miss Blow and her business. The police were very reticent. Sergeant Farrelly was an impressive man with a great deal of personal dignity. He knew that contemptible witticisms would be levelled at him and the force of which he was a member, if it came to be known that Miss Blow, a solitary young woman, had held up the police of Clonmore for the whole of one day and a part of the next. He dreaded the remarks of irreverent small boys if they heard how nearly he and his man had been forced to go in search of Dr O'Grady's body. He was haunted by a terrible fear that the story might get into the newspapers.

'There's them,' he said to Constable Cole, 'who'd be only too glad to get a handle against the police—fellows up in Dublin writing for low papers. Believe you me, it'll be mighty unpleasant for us if you aren't able to keep your mouth shut.'

Cole was no more willing than the sergeant to give information The inquirers, baffled at the barrack, moved on to the bar of the hotel, and asked their questions there. Jimmy O'Loughlin had no information to give them. He did not know, any better than his customers, the reason for Miss Blow's expedition; but he liked to pose as being well up in the whole business. He shook his head gravely, made cryptic remarks, parried questions with other questions, and at last, without in the least meaning to, conveyed the impression that Miss Blow, by some mysterious process of law, had been arrested for Dr O'Grady's debts. The opinion gained ground in the town as one after another of the inquirers emerged from the bar. Strong sympathy was felt with Miss Blow, and there was some talk of summoning a special meeting of the League to consider her case. It was generally agreed that a unanimous resolution would be appropriate, and that a series of questions might very well be asked in the House of Commons by one of the members for the county.

9

BEFORE any definite action was taken, the public interest was diverted from Miss Blow and her affairs by a new sensation. At about half-past one o'clock Mrs Patsy Devlin was seen advancing along the street towards the barrack with a crowd of women and children after her. Her appearance suggested that she was suffering from an extremity of grief. Her hair hung loose over her shoulders in picturesque grey wisps. Her bodice had only one fastening, a white pin, driven through it near the neck. Below the pin the garment gaped, down to the point at which, still gaping, it was tucked into a crimson petticoat. Her boots, a pair so large that they might have been, and probably were, her husband's, were unlaced, and clattered on the ground every time she lifted her feet.

'Himself is gone from me,' she wailed, when she reached the door of the barrack, 'gone and left me, and me sick in my bed with an impression on my chest and a rumbling within in the inside of me as it might be a cart, or two carts, and they with turf in them going along on the street.'

'My good woman,' said Sergeant Farrelly, 'go home out of this, and don't be making a disturbance on the public street.'

'Home, is it?' wailed Mrs Devlin; 'and where will I find a home when himself is gone from me?'

'Go to your bed,' said the sergeant; 'and if so be that you're sick the way you're after telling us, get the doctor to attend you.'

Then he recollected that there was no doctor in Clonmore, and suggested as an alternative that she should send one of the children up to Jimmy O'Loughlin's shop to buy 'some sort of a bottle that would do her good'.

'And what good would a bottle be to me, if I had the money, with himself gone from me? It was a bad head he was to me, and many's the time I've been sorry that I ever married him, but sure it's worse I'll do without him now he's gone.'

'And that's true for her, the creature,' said old Biddy Halloran from the outskirts of the crowd.

'Where is he gone to?' asked the sergeant.

'Is it where he has gone? If I knew that, would I come to you to find him for me? Where has he gone? Och, but I'd be the thankful woman this day if I could lay my eyes on him.'

Mrs Devlin wept wildly.

'Stop your crying, woman dear,' said a sympathizer; 'sure the police will have him found for you in two twos. Isn't that what they're here for?'

'When did you miss him?' asked the sergeant.

'Miss him! Amn't I missing him every minute since he went from me, and the children along with me crying for their da, and them with no da left them?'

'When did you see him last?' said the sergeant, varying the form of his question.

'I see him,' said Mrs Devlin, 'e'er last night. He came home, and him after spending the evening at Jimmy O'Loughlin's.'

'Had he drink taken?'

Mrs Devlin hesitated. One of her supporters in the crowd encouraged her to speak out boldly.

'Don't be afraid, Mrs Devlin, ma'am. Speak up to the sergeant when he asks you the question. It's for your own good that he's trying to get the truth out of you.'

'I won't,' said Mrs Devlin at last, 'be telling lies to you. He had not. There wasn't a sign of it on him, though I won't deny that he might have had a glass of porter or the like.'

'And did he spend the night with you in the house?'

'He did—he did,' wailed Mrs Devlin, overcome afresh by

the recollection. 'And in the morning, as it might be yesterday morning, when he had his breakfast took, "I'm off", says he, "up to the Castle," says he, "to see the old lord that always was a good friend to me and my father before me." And I never seen him since.'

'Did he go to the Castle?' asked the sergeant.

'How would I know whether he did or not? Amn't I after telling you that I was sick in my bed?'

'He did go,' said a man from the crowd, 'for I seen him getting over the wall into the deer park, and him looking most determined, the same as if he had business to do.'

'And why didn't you come up and tell me before?' asked the sergeant. 'He's gone for twenty-four hours and more, and it's only now you find it out.'

'I was expecting him to step into the house every minute,' said Mrs Devlin, 'and I wasn't willing to lay my mind down to it that he was gone, till there was no help for it.'

'The Lord save us!' said old Biddy Halloran. 'It's an afflicted creature you are this day, Mary Devlin.'

Sergeant Farrelly buttoned his tunic and took his cap. He summoned Constable Cole and they marched together down the street towards Jimmy O'Loughlin's hotel. The crowd, Mrs Devlin at the lead of it, followed them. Constable Cole turned.

'Go home out of that the lot of you,' he said, 'and take Mrs Devlin along with you. The matter is in the hands of the police now, and that ought to content you.'

Jimmy O'Loughlin's customers deserted him as soon as the noise of Mrs Devlin's wailing was heard in the street. He stood alone behind the bar when the police entered the hotel. He greeted the sergeant heartily, for he was a man of good conscience and unaware of any reason why he should dread a visit from the police. He was struck by the solemn severity with which Sergeant Farrelly replied to his greeting, and became vaguely uneasy. The business of a publican is beset with legal snares which only the most fortunate men succeed in avoiding altogether. Jimmy examined himself rapidly, but failed to discover anything in his immediate past which could bring him under the lash of the law. He was quite sure that batch of convivial friends who absorbed a few dozen bottles of porter on the previous Sunday had entered his house unseen. They had certainly entered it cautiously—by the back door—after climbing over a wall into his yard. His mental attitude was that of the people of the town of Bethlehem when the prophet Samuel came unexpectedly among them. They were not conscious of deserving any kind of denunciation, but they were anxious, and said to the great man: 'Comest thou peaceably?' Jimmy O'Loughlin might have repeated their exact words, but he had never heard the story, and was therefore unable to quote from it. His face wore an expression of anxious interrogation.

'Did you hear,' said Sergeant Farrelly, 'what they're after telling me about Patsy Devlin?'

'What about him?' said Jimmy cautiously.

'He's left the town and deserted his wife and family.'

'Do you say that now?'

'It's not me that says it,' said the sergeant; 'but it's being said.'

'I wouldn't wonder,' said Jimmy, 'but there might be some truth in it.'

Neither he nor his public-house could be held in any way responsible for the disappearance of Patsy Devlin. He felt free to discuss the event in a friendly way with the police and to give them any information he could so long as he said nothing likely to lead to the capture of Patsy.

'I'm told,' said the sergeant, 'that the last night he was in Clonmore he spent the most of it along with yourself.'

'He might,' said Jimmy.

He did not quite see the point of the sergeant's remark, and felt that he must be cautious.

'Could you give me any information about what he intended doing with himself the next day?'

'He told me,' said Jimmy, after thinking the matter over, 'and it could be that he was telling me the truth—he told me he was going up to the Castle to try if he could get a pound, or maybe two pounds, out of Lord Manton for the sports. He was collecting the town and the district; and he said to me himself that he'd done well. The money was coming in better than ever it did.'

'Ah!' said the sergeant with deep meaning.

'Just so,' said Jimmy.

'And was that what you meant this minute when you said that you wouldn't wonder if there might be some truth in what they're saying about him being gone?'

'He's not the first,' said Jimmy, 'nor he won't be the last. There was Cooney that was treasurer of the League, and nobody ever heard of him after. It was upwards of twenty pounds he had. There was——'

'It's larceny,' said Constable Cole.

'You're wrong there,' said the sergeant. 'It's misappropriation of public funds under trust, besides the charge that might be brought by the subscribers of obtaining money under false pretences.'

'You'll never get him,' said Jimmy.

'It isn't him I'm thinking of,' said the sergeant, 'but his wife that's left with a long family dependent on her and not knowing where to look for the bit to put into their mouths.'

'It's a pity of the creature,' said Constable Cole. 'It's badly she'll be able to do without him.'

'If so be,' said Jimmy, 'that Patsy's gone the way you say, he'll have left a trifle behind him for the widow, be the same more or less. He always had a good heart, and it wouldn't be like a thing he'd do to leave his children to starve.'

'Devil the penny she owned up to anyway,' said the sergeant.

'Then he'll send it,' said Jimmy; 'he'll send it from America.'

'He might,' said the sergeant.

'The world,' said Constable Cole, 'is full of trouble, any way you look at it.'

'Does Father Moroney know he's gone?' asked Jimmy.

'I'm thinking he must,' said the sergeant; 'he could hardly miss hearing the way the creature was going on in the street, crying all sorts.'

'He'll be apt to be raising a subscription for her,' said Jimmy, 'to put her over until such time as Patsy sends home the trifle he has for her.'

'I'll give something towards it myself,' said the sergeant, 'and I'll see that the men in the barrack contribute.'

Jimmy O'Loughlin was not to be outdone in generosity by the members of the constabulary.

'I have the pound by me,' he said, 'that I'd promised Patsy Devlin, the poor boy, for the sports. I hadn't it paid over to him, thanks be to God. I'd be thankful to you, sergeant, if you'd take it and hand it on to Father Moroney. It's no more than due to the woman, seeing that her husband could have had it if he'd thought of taking it, and I'll add another five shillings to it from myself.'

He handed the whole sum over to Sergeant Farrelly, who put it in his pocket.

'He was always a bit of a lad, that Patsy Devlin,' said Constable Cole.

'He might be a bit foolish at times,' said Jimmy; 'but there was no harm in him.'

'It's as good for you,' said the sergeant, 'that you didn't make him the inspector of sheep dipping that time.'

'It was that preyed on his mind,' said Jimmy. 'He never rightly got over it. I don't say he'd have been elected—there was better men up for the job than him—but he destroyed himself altogether when he went getting a testimonial to his character from Lord Manton. The League wouldn't stand the like of that, and small blame to them. It couldn't be expected that they would.'

'We'll go up to the Castle,' said the sergeant to Constable

Cole, 'and find out whether Patsy went there before he left, if so be that his lordship has come home.'

'I didn't hear any talk of his being away,' said Jimmy.

'Well he was away. Yesterday and today.'

'That's queer now,' said Jimmy, 'for it was only this morning I was talking to Byrne the steward, and he told me that his lordship was walking round yesterday afternoon looking into the new drain he's thinking of making across the top of the deer park, and that he went in for his tea the same as usual. What's more, he was speaking to Byrne this morning about the disgraceful way the roads is kept by the County Council, and the rates being so high and such-like.'

'It couldn't be,' said the sergeant, 'for I was up there three times yesterday, and I wasn't able to see him.'

'Take care but he didn't want to see you.'

'And I had a letter from him this morning telling me that he'd be away from home all the day.'

'Take care,' said Jimmy again, 'but he mightn't have wanted to see you.'

'And why wouldn't he?'

'I'm not saying it is, mind you,' said Jimmy; 'but it might be that he knows more about Patsy Devlin than he'd care to tell. Him and Patsy was mighty thick.'

'Talk sense, can't you?' said the sergeant. 'Is it likely now that a man like his lordship would be conniving at the escape of a criminal from justice?'

'I said no such thing,' said Jimmy; 'and I'll thank you, Sergeant Farrelly, not to be putting it out that I did. What I said was that he might know more than he'd care to tell. Would you think now that a gentleman like him—and I'll say this for him, that he always was a gentleman—do you think now that, if so be he did know where Patsy was gone, he'd be wanting to tell you and maybe get a poor man into trouble that he had a liking for? Didn't you tell me this minute that he had himself hid away from you when you were up at the

Castle looking for him? Why would he do the like? Tell me that now. Why would he do it?'

'Come along out of this,' said the sergeant to Constable Cole. 'We've no business standing here listening to such talk. I'm going up to the Castle now, Mr O'Loughlin, and if I hear so much as another word of that nonsense out of your head I'll tell his lordship what you're after saying.'

'You may tell him,' said Jimmy, 'when you get a hold of him to tell; but it's my belief that if he hid on you yesterday, he'll hide on you again today.'

It turned out that Jimmy O'Loughlin was perfectly right. Constable Cole said that he was prepared to swear, if necessary, that he saw Lord Manton looking out of one of the windows of the Castle. But Wilkins was as impenetrably suave as he had been the day before.

'His lordship left word,' he said, 'in case you called, that he was away from home and couldn't say precisely when he might return.'

I O

MR GODDARD, the District Inspector of Police, was a young man and stood on the lowest rung of his professional ladder. It was recognized by his superiors, it was even feared by the man himself, that he was never likely to rise very high in the service. He was, in fact, an inefficient officer. He had a natural sense of humour, which was a great misfortune, because it led him to see situations like those of comic operas in the course of the duties which he was called upon to perform. He was wise enough not to laugh loudly at the things which happened; but the fact that a great deal of what he had to do struck him as ludicrous prevented his doing his duty heartily and thoroughly. An Irish police officer ought to have a good opinion of himself and his position. He ought to recognize his official kinship with the potentates who draw large salaries for administering the affairs of the Indians, the Egyptians, and other barbarous peoples. He is humbler, of course, and is paid less; but he is engaged in the same kind of work. He is securing to a conquered people the blessings of law and order. Unfortunately, Mr Goddard could never see himself in this light. Another cause of his inefficiency was indolence. The duties which did not strike him as comic bored him intolerably; but like many lazy men, he was subject to spasms of vigour when irritated. It was his custom to avoid doing anything for as long as possible, and at last, if goaded beyond endurance, to act with a violence which surprised his subordinates. He had a taste for literature, even when it took the form of poetry, and used to read a good deal in the evenings.

He was reading a novel when Miss Blow and Constable Moriarty drove up to his house. He received them in his dining-room, and was chiefly anxious at first to get rid of them as soon as possible. He did not realize for some time that Miss Blow was the kind of woman who ought to be offered a chair and invited to sit down on it. She came, apparently, in the custody of a policeman, and Mr Goddard did not look closely at her. She saved him from any embarrassment he might afterwards have felt by walking over to an armchair and settling herself comfortably in it.

Constable Moriarty produced Lord Manton's note of complaint and handed it over to his officer. He explained that Sergeant Farrelly had called three times at Clonmore Castle and had waited in the hall for some hours in the hope of seeing Lord Manton. Mr Goddard read the note and asked a number of questions. He succeeded in greatly embarrassing

Constable Moriarty. That young man had the feelings of a gentleman. He would not say anything likely to cause pain or discomfort to a lady. He hesitated in his account of Miss Blow's invasion of the barrack. He contradicted himself three times in trying to explain the views of the police about the disappearance of Dr O'Grady.

Miss Blow cut into the conversation sharply.

'I demand,' she said, 'that the police should investigate a case of murder, and they refuse to do so.'

Mr Goddard, for the first time, took a good look at her. He realized at once that she was an extremely handsome girl. Even so it seemed improbable that any one would murder a dispensary doctor well known to be very popular.

'Murder,' he said tentatively, 'is perhaps too strong a word.'

'Lord Manton agrees with me,' said Miss Blow, 'that he has been murdered.'

She took Lord Manton's note from her pocket and handed it to Mr Goddard. He read it, re-read it, and then turned inquiringly to the constable. Moriarty reluctantly admitted that Lord Manton's words might bear the interpretation which Miss Blow put on them.

'Then why on earth did you not investigate the matter?' said Mr Goddard.

Constable Moriarty became very confused. With Miss Blow's fine eyes fixed on him he could not bring himself to blurt out the naked truth. He was as unwilling as everybody else had been to break the heart of a beautiful girl by saying that her lover had basely deserted her.

'It could be,' he said feebly, 'that the doctor's alive and well yet.'

This was very much Mr Goddard's own opinion. He read Lord Manton's note again, and then turned to Miss Blow.

'I am very sorry,' he said, 'that you should have been put to so much trouble and inconvenience. I hope I am not tiring you too much, but would you mind telling me what reasons you have for supposing that Dr O'Grady has been murdered?'

Miss Blow's eyes suddenly filled with tears. She caught at her skirt with both hands, clenching the folds of it tightly.

'We were to have been married this year,' she said, 'and oh——'

Then, fumbling hurriedly for her pocket-handkerchief she burst into a flood of tears. There was every excuse for her. She had been driven to the belief that her lover was murdered. She had gone through three trying days, the last two of them very trying. She was a stranger among people who seemed heartless and cruel to an extraordinary degree. She had every right to an outbreak of hysterical weeping. Yet it should be noted to her credit that she chose as the witness of her break-down the man, of all those whom she had met, most likely to be influenced by tears. Lord Manton, if she had wept in his study, would have comforted her; but he would also have en-joyed his task and would have appreciated the appearance of her slobbered cheeks. Sergeant Farrelly would have sym-pathized with her if she had wept in the police barrack, but he would not have gone out to search for Dr O'Grady's body merely because she made a sponge of her pocket-handkerchief. Mr Goddard was different. He was young, and though he had a sense of humour, the sight of a beautiful girl shaken with sobs embarrassed him.

He did not exactly know what he ought to do. He looked round, hoping for some suggestion from the constable; but Moriarty had slipped quietly from the room. Mr Goddard made a hasty and impassioned vow that he would give Constable Moriarty a severe lesson in the respect due to his superior officer. Then he looked at Miss Blow again. She was sobbing convulsively. He watched her helplessly for several minutes, and then asked her if she would like a cup of tea. He had to repeat the question twice, because, owing to ner-vousness, he was inaudible the first time he asked it. Miss Blow, when she heard what he said, shook her head vigorously. Mr Goddard felt that there must have been some-thing insulting about the suggestion, and was sorry he had made it. He wished very much that he knew how to behave under the circumstances. By way of relieving the tension of the situation he got up and stood behind Miss Blow. Then he walked round her chair and stood in front of her. Neither position availed to check her weeping. Her head was bowed almost to her lap and her face was covered with her hands. It occurred to him that it might soothe her if he patted her back and shoulders gently. He stretched out his hand. Then he paused. He was a man of chivalrous feeling towards women, the result perhaps of reading Tennyson's poetry, and it struck him that it would be unfair to pat a girl who was obviously incapable of resisting. He stood irresolute, his hand still stretched out. His attitude was not unlike that of a priest who bestows a benediction upon a deeply contrite penitent.

'Miss Blow,' he said at last, 'please stop crying.'

Curiously enough this appeal produced its effect upon her.

'How can I help crying,' she said, though her utterance was broken with sobs, 'when he's dead, and no one will help me even to find his body?'

Mr Goddard's resolution was taken in an instant. He did not believe that Dr O'Grady was dead. He knew that he was laying up trouble for himself in the future; but it was absolutely necessary to stop Miss Blow crying and, if possible, to get her out of the house.

'I'll help you,' he said. 'I'll do all that can be done to find him. I shall put all the men in my district to work. I shall leave no place unsearched until I find him, alive or dead.'

Miss Blow looked up at him and smiled through her tears. Even an ordinary girl, with no particular pretensions to beauty, looks very charming when she succeeds in smiling and crying at the same time. Miss Blow seemed radiantly lovely. Mr Goddard felt that he was losing command of himself. He felt strongly inclined to quote some poetry. He knew that there must be poetry suitable to the situation, but for the moment he could think of nothing except four lines out of *Maud*.

'Oh, that 'twere possible
    After long grief and pain
To feel the arms of my true love
    Around me once again.'

There was a certain appropriateness about the verses, and yet
he hesitated to quote them. He was not sure that Miss Blow
would care to admit in plain words to a total stranger that she
wanted Dr O'Grady's arm round her. Miss Blow saved him
from his uncertainty. She gave her eyes two rapid dabs with
her wet pocket-handkerchief, and said—

'When shall we start?'

'Some day next week,' said Mr Goddard. 'Suppose we
say——'

Miss Blow collapsed again, and showed every sign of more
tears.

'Sooner, if you like,' said Mr Goddard hurriedly.

'At once, then,' said Miss Blow, rallying; 'at once; this very
moment.'

Mr Goddard looked at his watch. It was three o'clock. It
would take him at least two hours to drive to Clonmore. He
could do very little there that evening.

'At once,' repeated Miss Blow; 'this very instant.'

Mr Goddard gave in. He believed that he was going to
make a fool of himself, but he saw no way of escape. Miss
Blow's vigorous manner of crying convinced him that she was
quite capable of sitting in his dining-room and continuing to
cry until he set out in search of Dr O'Grady's body.

'Will you excuse me,' he said, 'while I go upstairs and put
on my uniform?'

Miss Blow nodded and smiled again. The thought of a uniform comforted her. A man can hardly fail in his duty when
he puts on a uniform for the express purpose of performing it.
Mr Goddard took courage from her smile.

'I shall tell my housekeeper,' he said, 'to bring you a cup of
tea. I am sure you must need it. You can drink it while you

are waiting. I shall have my horse harnessed and drive you back with me to Clonmore.'

This time Miss Blow did not refuse the tea. She drank two cups of it when it was brought to her, and finished a plate of bread-and-butter. It took Mr Goddard some time to array himself, because he paused frequently to try and hit upon some way of getting rid of Miss Blow without driving her into Clonmore. He tried in vain. Miss Blow, after drinking her tea, was able to devote a few minutes to her hair and the position of her hat. There was a mirror over the chimney-piece in Mr Goddard's dining-room.

Mr Goddard's horse was a good one, and could undoubtedly have done the journey to Clonmore in less than two hours, but Mr Goddard did not press him. He found the drive agreeable. Miss Blow had quite stopped crying before she got into the trap, and she talked with the utmost frankness about her affairs. There is something very delightful in the confidences of a beautiful girl.

Miss Blow had a way of looking up with her eyes wide open, which sent a curious thrill of pleasure through Mr Goddard. There was only one thing which marred the enjoy-ment of the drive. Her confidences were of the most puzzling and embarrassing kind. She told how everybody in Clonmore had lied. And so far, Mr Goddard sympathized with her. But he could not help asking himself why they had lied. Even Jimmy O'Loughlin, as Mr Goddard understood, would not lie persistently without a motive of some kind. Of course, Miss Blow had an explanation already at hand. Dr O'Grady was murdered, and everybody was interested in concealing the fact. But Mr Goddard could not believe this. He did not attempt to argue with her, for he had no wish to reduce her to tears again; but he knew very well that nobody in the neighbourhood would murder Dr O'Grady. He was inclined at first to think, as every one else did, that the doctor had run away from his creditors; but Miss Blow demonstrated the absurdity of this theory. She had come to Clonmore with a blank cheque signed by her father, and full authority to pay every penny the doctor owed. She had told him beforehand in a letter that he might expect some relief. Mr Goddard was forced to admit that under the circumstances it was very unlikely that Dr O'Grady had allowed himself to be chased away to America by his creditors.

At the same time, the doctor had undoubtedly disappeared. That seemed the one solid fact there was. Miss Blow referred frequently to Lord Manton's note. It puzzled Mr Goddard quite as much as anything else did. He knew Lord Manton, and he could not understand how he came to believe, as apparently he did believe, in the murder of Dr O'Grady. Mr Goddard made up his mind that he would go up to Clonmore Castle and talk the whole matter over with Lord Manton. This was the solitary decision he was able to come to; though he was obliged to pledge himself over and over again to institute a strict search for the doctor's body. He arrived at last in Clonmore and drove straight up to the hotel.

'You must be very tired,' he said to Miss Blow, 'quite worn out. Now that the matter is in my hands, you need have no further anxiety. I hope you will stay quietly in the hotel and rest till I see you again.'

He spoke quite sincerely. He did hope that Miss Blow would go to the hotel and stay there. He feared that she might feel it necessary to follow him about and watch what he did.

'I shall inform you at once,' he went on, 'of everything which transpires. I must spend this evening in making some preliminary inquiries; but there is no necessity for you to fatigue yourself further.'

Miss Blow looked at him long and searchingly. Mr Goddard felt that she was judging of his strength and determination, was deciding whether she could fully trust him or not. He endeavoured to assume the expression of face which he believed to be common to those strong, silent Englishmen, whom the heroines of novels learn, after other people have turned out to be frauds, to trust to the uttermost. He was, apparently, quite successful in his effort. He deserved to be; for he really felt for the moment, with Miss Blow's eyes on him, that he was exactly the kind of man he wished to appear. Miss Blow, without a word, stretched out her hand to him. He took it and ventured to press it slightly. He would have carried it to his lips and pressed a reverent kiss upon it, if Jimmy O'Loughlin had not been standing at the door of the hotel. Afterwards he was very sorry that he had not defied Jimmy O'Loughlin. A reverent kiss, even if it had to soak through a glove, would have been most appropriate to the occasion.

Miss Blow got out of the trap and went into the hotel. Mr Goddard drove on to the police barrack.

He found Sergeant Farrelly and Constable Cole drawn up before the door. They had seen their inspector drive into the town and were ready for him. Mr Goddard at once ordered the sergeant to follow him into the barrack. Constable Cole mounted guard over the horse and trap.

'Now, sergeant,' said Mr Goddard, 'what have you to tell me about the disappearance of Dr O'Grady?'

'There's another man gone since then, sir,' said the sergeant gloomily.

'What do you mean? Who's gone?'

'I thought it right to let you know, sir—I was within writing a report on the matter when I seen you drive into the town—that Patsy Devlin the smith is gone. His wife was up at the barrack shortly after Constable Moriarty left with the young lady, and she says he's missing.'

'It's a queer thing,' said Mr Goddard, 'that two men should disappear in this sort of way within a couple of days of each other. It looks bad. Let's take them one at a time and see what we can make out of them. What have you to say about the doctor?'

'Everybody knows the reason he's made off,' said the sergeant, 'only nobody'd like to be telling the young lady, and that's what has us all put about the way we are.'

'Do you mean debt?'

'I do, sir. It's a common talk. Jimmy O'Loughlin told me himself——'

'It's not true anyhow, whether Jimmy O'Loughlin said it or not. Whatever it was made the doctor bolt, it wasn't that.'

'Then I don't know what it would be.'

'No more do I; but I'm going to see Lord Manton and talk to him about it.'

'It could be,' said Sergeant Farrelly, 'that he'd know. Did you take notice of the note that he gave to the young lady?'

'Yes; I saw it.'

'Well now, his lordship couldn't be believing that the doctor's murdered, and whatever made him write that note it's my opinion that there was something behind it. And what's more, Jimmy O'Loughlin says——'

'Damn Jimmy O'Loughlin!'

'Jimmy O'Loughlin says,' went on the sergeant, 'that his lordship knows something, be the same more or less, about Patsy Devlin. I wouldn't wonder now if he'd be able to tell you where the both of the two of them is gone and why.'

'What about Patsy Devlin?' asked Mr Goddard. 'What sort of a man is he?'

'He's no great things any way you take him. He's a bit foolish at times, and takes more than is good for him. I hear them say that he fretted a deal when they didn't make him the inspector of sheep dipping. It might be that the disappointment preyed on him, that and the drink, so as he wouldn't be rightly responsible for what he did.'

'Was he mixed up with the League?'

'He was at one time, but there was a falling out between him and them over the sheep dipping. Patsy wasn't what you'd call great with the League since then. I'm told he had a deal of money collected for the sports. Jimmy O'Loughlin let out to me that——'

'It seems to me,' said Mr Goddard, 'that Jimmy O'Loughlin

knows more about these disappearances than anybody else about the place.'

'Unless it would be Lord Manton,' said the sergeant.

'I'll see Lord Manton anyhow,' said Mr Goddard. 'You can tell the constable to take my horse and trap round to the hotel. I'll walk up to the Castle.'

'It'll be well,' said the sergeant, 'if you get seeing his lord-ship.'

He spoke meaningly. Mr Goddard, who was half way to the barrack door, turned back.

'What's that you say?'

'It'll be well,' said the sergeant, 'if you're not told that his lordship's away from home.'

'What do you mean by that?'

'I was up there, yesterday,' said the sergeant; 'off and on I was there for the most of the day; and I was up there again today, and all I got by it was word that his lordship was away from home. Jimmy O'Loughlin was saying——'

'Go on,' said Mr Goddard, 'Jimmy O'Loughlin's remarks are always valuable.'

'He was saying that his lordship was within all the time. It was his opinion—I'm not saying was he right or wrong—but it was his opinion that his lordship didn't want the police next or nigh him.'

'Jimmy O'Loughlin,' said Mr Goddard, 'appears to be as big a fool as anybody about Clonmore.'

WILKINS was a little puzzled when he opened the door to Mr Goddard. His orders were definite. Lord Manton was not at home when the police called. Mr Goddard in his uniform, complete to the sword, the whistle and the spurs, was undeniably a policeman. But Wilkins was a good servant. He was accustomed to interpreting orders as well as obeying them. He knew that Mr Goddard was a superior kind of policeman. He dined occasionally at Clonmore Castle, and Wilkins waited on him. After a moment's hesitation, Wilkins offered to go and find out whether Lord Manton was at home or not. Mr Goddard was shown into a large, desolate drawing-room, and left there. Wilkins was glad afterwards that he had appreciated the difference in standing between a district inspector and a sergeant. It appeared that Lord Manton was quite willing to see this visitor. Mr Goddard was shown into the library.

'Sit down,' said Lord Manton, 'I'm very glad to see you. You'll stay and dine, won't you? Since poor O'Grady left us I haven't had a soul to speak to at meals.'

'It was about Dr O'Grady's disappearance that I called to see you,' said Mr Goddard.

'There's no use coming to me about that. I'm a magistrate, I know; but I very seldom act. Why not go to Jimmy O'Loughlin? He loves signing papers.'

'I'm rather puzzled over the case. The fact is——'

'My advice to you is to leave it alone. Don't do anything. Masterly inactivity is plainly the policy for you.'

'That's all well enough. I'd be very glad to leave it alone. There's nothing I'd like better. But the fact is, I can't. I'm more or less pledged to——. My hand has been, so to speak, forced.'

'Had a visit from Miss Blow?'

'Yes.'

'She's a wonderful woman. She was here yesterday; spent half an hour with me in this very room.'

'She's a very good-looking girl,' said Mr Goddard.

'She is. I admit that. Her eyes, for instance. Grey, I thought them; but they looked quite blue in certain lights; and a very good figure, a remarkable figure. All the same I couldn't have her settling herself down for good and all in my house. I had to get her out of it somehow. I gave her a note for Sergeant Farrelly.'

'Oh! That's the meaning of your note. It rather puzzled me.'

'I'm afraid it must have rather puzzled Sergeant Farrelly too. I felt sorry for him; but what could I do? She evidently meant to stay here till I gave her a note of the sort she wanted. I thought it better to shift the responsibility of dealing with her on to the sergeant. After all, he's paid for looking into things of the kind. I'm not.'

'The sergeant sent her on to me. It was extremely awkward. She cried like anything.'

'I thought she'd have cried here,' said Lord Manton; 'but she didn't. Did you comfort her?'

'No, I didn't. At least I suppose I did in the end. I didn't know what to do. I'm not a married man, and I'm not accustomed to——'

'How did you comfort her in the end? It would interest me very much to hear, if the details are of the sort that will bear repeating without giving Miss Blow away. Did you hold a pocket handkerchief to her eyes?'

'No, nothing of that kind. I——' Mr Goddard hesitated.

'Go on,' said Lord Manton. 'I'll treat whatever you say as strictly confidential.'

'Well, I promised to do what she asked.'

107

'Do you mean to say that you've pledged yourself to go searching the country for Dr O'Grady's body?'

'I couldn't help it. What on earth else could I do?'

'And when do you start?'

'I don't mean to start at all.'

Lord Manton pretended not to hear this remark.

'Do the thing in style if you do it at all,' he said. 'Get blood-hounds. I'll give you the address of a man in England who breeds them. Fish out an old sock of the doctor's; let the bloodhound get the scent, and then we'll all be off across country.'

'I don't mean to do any such fool thing.'

'We'll have glorious paragraphs in all the papers,' said Lord Manton. ' "MYSTERIOUS DISAPPEARANCE OF A DOCTOR. VIGOROUS ACTION OF THE ROYAL IRISH CONSTABULARY. DISTRICT INSPECTOR GODDARD THINKS HE HAS A CLUE. BLOODHOUNDS USED. FIANCÉE IN TEARS." Your portrait will appear along with Miss Blow's.'

'It's all very fine to laugh,' said Mr Goddard; 'but of course I'm not going——'

'You'll have to. You've promised. You can't go back on a promise made to a lady. Her portrait will be published in the papers and everybody will see how charming she is. You'll be an object of universal hatred and contempt if you go back on your word.'

'If ever it gets into the papers at all, you'll look quite as great a fool as I shall. Your note will be published. And, after all, you know, the girl has something to say for herself. The doctor's gone. Now, why the devil did he go, and where has he gone to?'

'Can't you give a guess at his motives?'

'No, I can't. It wasn't debt. Miss Blow told me herself that she was ready to pay every penny that he owed.'

'No; it's not debt. I thought it was at first, but it appears I was wrong.'

'He didn't drink,' said Mr Goddard, 'that ever I heard of.

Besides, even if he did, that would be no reason for bolting. Whisky's as plenty here as anywhere in the world.'

'No; it's not drink. Try the other thing. There's only one more. "Love, or debt, or whisky"—you know the old saying. If it isn't either of the last two, it must be the first.'

'Love!' said Mr Goddard.

'Precisely.'

'But, hang it all! Miss Blow's quite ready to marry him.'

'Too ready,' said Lord Manton; 'that's my point.'

Mr Goddard thought hard for a couple of minutes.

'Do you mean to suggest,' he said at last, 'that he's run away from her?'

'In the absence of any other conceivable reason for his bolting,' said Lord Manton, 'I am unwillingly driven to the conclusion that he wants to escape from Miss Blow.'

'But, hang it all! Why should he be? The girl's uncommonly good-looking.'

'Good looks aren't everything,' said Lord Manton; 'when you come to my time of life, you'll understand that. Just put yourself in the doctor's place for a minute. You've had some little experience of Miss Blow. So have I. But the poor doctor knew her a great deal better than we do. Just think of what his feelings must have been when he heard that she was coming over here to pay his debts. He'd be bound to marry her straight off after that. And then—just think of sitting down to breakfast every morning opposite a young woman of her character. I admit her good looks, but she's masterful. She'd bully a prize-fighter. The poor doctor wouldn't have had the ghost of a chance, especially as married life would begin by her paying his debts. That would give her the whip hand of him at once; and she's just the sort of girl who would make the most of her opportunities.'

'I don't know—it's possible, of course.'

'It's certain, man. Be reasonable. Here's a fact, a perfect undeniable fact. The doctor's gone. Unless you're going to adopt Miss Blow's hypothesis——'

'Oh, he's not murdered, of course. I know that.'

'Very well, then, my explanation of his disappearance is the only one that's left. And it's quite a probable one in itself. Nine men out of ten in the doctor's position would do exactly what he's done.'

'Then what the devil am I to do?'

'You're in a deuced awkward position. I don't know what the end of it will be. The authorities certainly won't stand your taking the police away from their ordinary duties, and setting them to scour the country for the body of a man who isn't dead. There'd be questions asked in Parliament about it, and all sorts of fuss. Besides, you'd look such an ass.'

'I know I should.'

'All the same, you're in for it now. Unless you choose to go and tell Miss Blow the truth. She might believe you, though I very much doubt it.'

'I couldn't possibly do that. No man could tell a girl that her—— But, look here, Lord Manton, your theory may be all very well so far as O'Grady is concerned; but there's another man gone now.'

'Patsy Devlin,' said Lord Manton. 'I heard about that.'

'Do you think he has run away through fear of his wife?'

'No, I don't. There are plenty of other ways of accounting for his disappearance. Besides, in the case of Mrs Devlin—you know her, perhaps?'

'No; I never set eyes on the woman in my life.'

'Well, she's not equal to Miss Blow in personal appearance; but she has a certain charm of her own. You wouldn't meet a quieter, less obtrusive sort of woman anywhere. Nobody would run away from her unless he was forced to. You take my word for it, Patsy will send word for her to follow him wherever he's gone to. I knew both Patsy and his wife well, and they always got on splendidly together. The poor fellow was something of a *protégé* of mine. I think he regarded me as a friend, and was inclined to confide in me. I gave him a letter of recommendation to the Board of Guardians, at the time of the election of the inspector of sheep dipping.'

'I understood from Sergeant Farrelly,' said Mr Goddard, 'that the man was rather a blackguard.'

'A horrid blackguard,' said Lord Manton. 'That's why I didn't want them to elect him.'

'But I thought you said——'

'So I did; but there's no use discussing that now. It's all over and done with. Poor Patsy will never inspect the dipping of a single sheep now. Besides, it's almost dinner-time. You'll stay, of course. Never mind about dressing.'

Mr Goddard was tempted. Lord Manton would give him a good dinner; Jimmy O'Loughlin—and the choice lay between the two—would almost certainly give him a bad one. Inclination struggled with conscience. In the end conscience prevailed.

'I can't,' he said. 'I must see Miss Blow this evening.'

'Oh, of course, if you have an appointment with Miss Blow —I suppose the poor doctor won't mind now.'

'You're quite wrong. I haven't that sort of an appointment at all. The simple fact is that I'm afraid of her. If I don't see her and manage to keep her quiet somehow, she'll be over at the barrack again making a nuisance of herself. You couldn't tell what she'd do.'

'She might take it into her head that you were murdered, and set everybody searching for your body.'

'She might do anything. That's the reason I won't stay to dine with you, though I'd like to.'

'Good night,' said Lord Manton. 'Let me know how things go on; and if you are driven to bloodhounds, remember that I can put you on to the best in England.'

When Mr Goddard got back to the hotel, he found that his self-sacrifice was wasted. Miss Blow had retired to her room for the night.

'It could be,' said Jimmy O'Loughlin, 'that the young lady was tired. "Bridgy," says she, when she came in, "I'm off up to my bed; and I'd be thankful to you if you'd bring me up a cup of tea when it's convenient to Mrs O'Loughlin to wet it." '

This did not sound like a thing Miss Blow would have said. Mr Goddard felt that Jimmy O'Loughlin was adding a varnish of politeness to the original remark. The next words reassured him. There was at least a foundation of fact beneath the version of the story which he had heard.

' "And take care," says she, "that the kettle's boiling, for the last cup of tea you made for me was poison, and smoked at that." '

The words were not yet the words of Miss Blow, but the meaning might very well have been hers.

'She's mighty particular about her tea,' said Jimmy. 'She has the life fair plagued out of Bridgy; not but what Bridgy deserves it. And what would you be wishing for yourself, Mr Goddard?'

Mr Goddard wished that he had accepted Lord Manton's invitation. Since it appeared that Miss Blow was safely in her room, perhaps actually in bed, he might just as well have dined in comfort at Clonmore Castle. But he did not make this reply to Jimmy O'Loughlin. He said that what he was wishing for himself was a chop and a bottle of porter. He might have said whisky instead of porter, but he knew that there was no hope of getting anything else in the way of food except the chop. Jimmy O'Loughlin accepted the order and ushered his guest into the commercial room, which happened to be empty.

In due time Bridgy entered with the chop. It was served on a plate with a round tin cover over it; a cover which meant well, but failed to keep the chop warm. Mr Goddard contemplated the frozen grease which clung round the edges of the plate, and then, lest it too should freeze, plunged his knife and fork into the chop. Bridgy uncorked his bottle of porter, and set it on the table beside a dish of potatoes. Yellow froth oozed rapidly from the mouth of the bottle and ran down on to the table-cloth. It added one more brown stain to those which the last four commercial travellers, eating in haste, had made with Worcester sauce, mustard, and gravy. Mr Goddard, who had a fastidious dislike of dirty table linen, seized the bottle, and then discovered that he had no tumbler. He set the bottle in the fender, and rang the bell furiously. Bridgy half opened the door, and put her head into the room. The rest of her body remained outside. This was her ordinary way of presenting herself to people who rang bells. She looked as if she expected to have plates thrown at her, and meant to be ready for a swift retreat.

'A tumbler,' said Mr Goddard.

Bridgy smiled pleasantly. 'It's hardly ever,' she said, 'I lay the table but I do be forgetting something. It might be the salt, or have you the salt? Glory be to God! you have, and the spoon along with it.'

There was a pool of considerable size in the fender round the porter bottle, and the froth was still oozing out persistently.

'A tumbler,' said Mr Goddard again.

His tone startled Bridgy. She disappeared, closing the door behind her. In a few minutes she was back again without the tumbler.

'Where is it?' said Mr Goddard.

'The mistress is giving it a bit of a rinse the way it'll be clean for you; and I came back to tell you that Mr Moriarty from the barrack below is at the door, and he says he wants to see you. I'm thinking it's a telegram that he has in his hand.'

Mr Goddard rose. 'Get a cloth,' he said, 'if there is a cloth in the house——'

'Sure there is,' murmured Bridgy, 'there's dozens.'

'And mop up that abominable mess. Take the chop down to the kitchen and heat it up again. Get another bottle of porter; and for heaven's sake let me have a meal that I can eat when I come back.'

He went out and discovered Constable Moriarty, who had, as Bridgy observed, a telegram in his hand.

'It came, sir,' said the constable, 'and you just after leaving Ballymoy with the young lady. The sergeant beyond said I'd better bring it with me the way you'd get it at once, in case it might be important.'

Mr Goddard opened it. 'From Inspector-General, Dublin Castle,' he read. 'Party of Members of Parliament arrive Clonmore tomorrow, noon, from Dublin. On tour. Provide vehicles to meet train. Show every attention. Five in party.'

'Damn it!' said Mr Goddard.

Every one in Ireland had heard of the tour of the Members of Parliament. It was well advertised by means of paragraphs in all the daily papers, so well advertised that an exaggerated opinion was formed in Ireland of the importance of the party. It was generally believed—and the language of the newspapers fostered the delusion—that at least two Cabinet Ministers were coming, ten or twelve influential politicians, and that more than the usual number of journalists would be in attendance. It was felt that the tour offered a unique opportunity for producing a lasting effect on English public opinion. There was, consequently, a severe struggle in Dublin among the numerous people who wanted to conduct the strangers round Ireland. Not only all the heads of all the Boards and Departments, but all the Presidents and Secretaries of the Leagues and Associations unconnected with Government were anxious to secure the honour. In the end it fell to a high official, who, in order to obtain it, made what was felt to be an unfair use of the influence he possessed in England. When he found at the last moment that the party consisted after all of only two Members of Parliament, and they men of inferior calibre and no real standing, he was disgusted and withdrew his offer of a motor car. When he found, further, that there were to be no journalists, and that the Members of Parliament were to be accompanied by three women, two wives and one aunt, he lost his temper and offered the party to any League which liked to apply for it. In the end he made over his whole responsibility to the police. The party went from place to place in the usual way. It was met at railway stations by polite inspectors of police, allowed to ask questions of the people who could be relied upon to supply the proper answers, and given opportunity of seeing with its own eyes the things that inquiring Englishmen ought to see. The Members enjoyed themselves immensely, and insisted on prolonging their tour after all the places originally marked out for them had been visited. Then the Inspector-General of Police, who was getting tired of making arrangements for them, sent them to Clonmore. It was a very distant place, the terminus of the line of railway on which it stood, and it was supposed that no harm could possibly come of their visiting it. They were told to drive from Clonmore round a particularly desolate coast, to stop at hotels which were quite abominable, and to pick up another railway fifty miles off. The Inspector-General reckoned that the trip would take at least four days, and that at the end of it the party would have had enough of Ireland. In any case he would not be bothered with them again until they reached the fifty miles distant railway station.

When Mr Goddard read the telegram he was greately irritated. He did not want to conduct a party of Members of Parliament round Clonmore, and their coming would certainly not help him to deal with Miss Blow. He foresaw frightful complications. It was possible that the Members of Parliament, rejoicing in the unexpected discovery of a side of Irish life hitherto unknown to them, might insist on joining in the search for the body of Dr O'Grady. He determined, if he possibly could, to prevent their arrival. He went back into the hotel and wrote a telegram.

'Inspector-General of Police, Dublin. This district quite unsuited to Members of Parliament. Am investigating cases of mysterious disappearance. Inhabitants greatly excited. Disaffection feared. Send party elsewhere.'

'Take this,' he said to Constable Moriarty, 'and dispatch it at once.'

'The office shuts at eight, sir,' said the constable; 'but I'll see that it's sent off first thing in the morning.'

Mr Goddard looked at his watch. It was twenty minutes to

nine o'clock. At eight the next morning the party would leave Dublin. He swore again and tore up his telegram.

I 2

MR GODDARD met Miss Blow at breakfast next morning, and nerved himself to the task of telling her that the search for Dr O'Grady's body must be put off for twenty-four hours on account of the visit of the Members of Parliament to the district. He did not know exactly how she would take the news. He half hoped that she might get angry and say something which would give him an excuse for washing his hands of her affairs. He feared that she might cry again as she had cried in his dining-room the day before. He did not want to comfort her under Jimmy O'Loughlin's roof. Either Bridgy or Mrs O'Loughlin might enter the room at any moment. Even Jimmy himself, under some pretext, might interrupt the affecting scene. Mr Goddard was conscious that an account of his dealings with a tearful Miss Blow given by Jimmy O'Loughlin would add to the gaiety of the neighbourhood. His hope, as it turned out, was quite vain and his fear unfounded. Miss Blow took the news in a most unexpected way.

'I'm glad to hear it,' she said.

Mr Goddard was surprised. Miss Blow explained herself, and he came to see that she had not given up her plan of a search party. It appeared that she had a very high regard for Members of Parliament. Next to the Habeas Corpus Act, which did not apply in Dr O'Grady's case because no one knew who had the body, and trial by jury, a notoriously uncertain thing in Ireland, she looked to Parliament as the great safeguard of individual rights and liberties.

It became obvious to Mr Goddard that Miss Blow expected the touring Members to take up her case at once and vigorously, perhaps to make a special law about it on the spot. He tried to explain that these particular Members were travelling unofficially. Miss Blow did not seem to think that fact made any difference. A Member of Parliament, according to her view, is a Member of Parliament, whether he is actually delivering a vote at Westminster or not. Mr Goddard then gave it as his opinion that there were too few Members of Parliament in the party to do anything effective.

'It isn't,' he said, 'as if we had enough of them to constitute a majority of the House.'

Miss Blow, by way of reply, stated her intention of meeting the party at the railway station. She said she was sure that as soon as they heard her story they would bestir themselves just as Lord Manton and Mr Goddard had, but rather more vigorously. She even suggested that a telegram might be sent to the Prime Minister. Mr Goddard discouraged her. He felt that he was being rapidly edged into a very awkward position. It was utterly impossible to calculate the effect that a story like Miss Blow's might produce on an enthusiastic Member of Parliament. Almost anything might happen. Publicity, newspaper paragraphs, and questions in the House of Commons would be certainties. And he had been warned to show the approaching party every civility. It would certainly not be civil to plunge them into a vortex of mysterious crime. The Inspector-General would naturally be vexed if such a thing happened, and Mr Goddard's prospects of promotion, never very brilliant, would be injured.

'I don't think it would do,' he said, 'for you to meet them at the railway station.'

'Why not?'

The Miss Blow at the other side of the breakfast table with

a teapot in front of her and a decisive way of handling it seemed quite different from the Miss Blow who had wept so pleasingly in his dining-room the day before.

'I rather think,' he said feebly, 'that they have ladies with them.'

'All the better,' said Miss Blow.

'And their tour is quite unofficial. We're not supposed to know that they're Members of Parliament.'

'But we do know,' said Miss Blow.

The argument ended by Mr Goddard promising to lay the case before the Members. It was only by making the promise that he was able to induce Miss Blow to refrain from going to the railway station. Having made it he slipped out of the room. It was after ten o'clock, and he still had to make arrangements for the comfort of the party. He found Jimmy O'Loughlin in the yard behind the hotel.

'There's a party coming by the train today,' he said, 'and I want a brake and four horses to meet them. They'll be driving to Pool-a-donagh.'

'Is it the Lord Lieutenant?' said Jimmy O'Loughlin.

'No, it's not. It's a private party.'

'I asked the question,' said Jimmy, 'because, if it was the Lord Lieutenant itself, he couldn't get the brake.'

'Oh, well, that's all right. It's not the Lord Lieutenant.'

'And if the Lord Lieutenant wouldn't get it,' said Jimmy, 'you may take your oath that another won't.'

'And why not?'

'Because the two front wheels is off the only brake there is in the town, and Patsy Devlin has them up at the forge fixing them, and he's gone from us. That's why.'

'And there isn't another brake?'

'There is not.'

'There are five in the party,' said Mr Goddard. 'We'll have to get two cars.'

'It's a good eight miles to Rosivera,' said Jimmy, 'and better than ten on from that to Pool-a-donagh. I wouldn't say that there was a horse in the town fit to do the journey with four on the car, and there'll have to be four on one of the cars, if there's five in the party, that'll be counting the drivers. My own mare was over at Ballymoy yesterday with Constable Moriarty and the doctor's young lady. It's a day's rest she ought to have by rights, and not be going off on the road again.'

'It can't be helped,' said Mr Goddard. 'I must have the horses.'

'There isn't another gentleman about the country,' said Jimmy, 'that I'd do it for only yourself; but seeing that the party is friends of your own, I'll let my mare go, and I'll get Patsy Devlin's grey pony that was promised to Mr Byrne for the day to be carting home the turf, the same pony that the priest was thinking of buying. It's little use Patsy's widow will have for a pony now that her husband's gone from her, the creature. I don't know another that you could put under a side car for a gentleman to sit behind, and it's badly able for the road the grey pony will be this minute.'

'Give her a feed of oats between this and the time the train comes in,' said Mr Goddard.

'I will; and I'll see if I can't get the loan of the priest's cushions for the old car. The ones that are on it are terrible bad.'

Jimmy O'Loughlin was certainly not guilty of raising any false hopes about the quality of his cattle or his vehicles: but Mr Goddard had a feeling of cold disgust when he saw the two cars standing together outside the railway station. Jimmy O'Loughlin's mare was the better of the two animals, and she looked extraordinary feeble and depressed. The grey pony, which should have been drawing home Mr Byrne's turf, was clearly unfit for the journey before him. He may have been fretting for the loss of Patsy Devlin. He may have been in-sufficiently fed by Mrs Devlin. He looked as if his spirit was completely broken either by starvation or great grief. The cars were dilapidated, and the harness evidently untrustworthy. On the other hand the drivers were full of life and vigour. They looked forward to receiving handsome tips from the strangers at the end of their day's work, and were quite prepared to earn them by saying all the things which tourists expect from Irish car drivers. They were primed with stories of the most popular kind about every point of interest along the road. They had a store of bulls and humorous repartees ready to their lips. They touched their hats jauntily to Mr Goddard as he passed them. He was a benefactor, and they owed him respect and thanks.

The train drew up at the platform. The door of a first-class compartment was flung open, and a gentleman bounded from it. His face expressed a feeling of irresponsible holiday happiness. His movements and the pose of his body suggested abundant vitality and energy. He turned and assisted three ladies to alight. One, the youngest of them, he lifted out in his arms and deposited three or four paces from the carriage door. He laughed merrily as he did so. She also laughed. The other two ladies, who had not been embraced, laughed. The holiday spirit was strong in all of them. Then, still laughing, he turned to the carriage again, and received from someone inside a number of bags, boxes, coats and parcels. He took them two by two and laid them in a long row at the feet of the ladies. Then a second gentleman got out of the train, a long, lean man, of sallow complexion and serious expression.

Mr. Goddard felt that it was time to introduce himself. He approached the party cautiously, skirting an outlying hold-all. The first gentleman, who was also a good deal the younger of the two, spied him coming and bounded forward to meet him.

'You are Mr Goddard,' he said joyously. 'I'm sure you must be. I'm delighted to meet you. My name is Dick, surname, you know. Christian name similar—Richard. Richard Dick, M.P., not yet in the Cabinet.'

He had to the highest possible degree that air of breezy joviality assumed by many Englishmen when they cross St

George's Channel. It was as if, having at last reached the land of frolicsome recklessness, he was determined to show himself capable of wild excess and a very extremity of Celtic fervour.

Mr Goddard bowed, and murmured that he felt it a pleasure and an honour to make Mr Dick's acquaintance.

'This,' said Mr Dick, 'is Mr Sanders. Sorrowful Sanders we call him, on account of the expression of his face. He's not in the Cabinet either; but he soon will be.' He caught Mr Goddard by the arm and whispered a clearly audible aside. 'He's a Scot, and that's nearly the same thing, you know.'

'Shut up, Dick!' said Mr Sanders.

'How can you talk such nonsense?' said the eldest of the three ladies, whose appearance suggested some strength of character, and suddenly brought back Miss Blow to Mr Goddard's mind.

'This,' said Mr Dick, indicating the lady, 'is Miss Farquharson, Sander's aunt. This'—he pointed to another lady—'is Mrs Sanders, his wife. And this'—he drew forward by the hand the lady whom he had lifted out of the carriage—'is Mrs Dick, the "woman that owns me." Isn't that the way you express it in this country?'

Mr Goddard bowed three times, and then glanced doubtfully at the bags which lay on the platform.

'I've only been able to get two cars for you,' he said. 'Have you much more luggage in the van?'

'Oh, but an Irish car can carry any quantity of luggage,' said Miss Farquharson. 'I've seen them absolutely packed, and still there was room for more.'

Mr Goddard admitted that this was true; but he thought of Patsy Devlin's grey pony and the long miles between Clonmore and Pool-a-donagh.

'And if there isn't room,' said Mrs Dick. 'I'd like to sit in the middle—on the well—isn't that what they call it?—with my back against the driver. I saw a boy sitting like that the other day, and it looked lovely.'

'It's all right,' said Mr Dick. 'We have two bikes with us. Sanders and I will ride. You shall have my machine, Sanders, and I'll take my wife's. Come along. The spin will do you all the good in the world. We'll pedal along and let the ladies have the cars.'

Mr Sanders protested strongly against this plan. He had, he said, a weak heart, and cycling did not agree with him. He was overborne by a command from his aunt, and towed down the platform towards the luggage van by Mr Dick. Miss Farquharson confided to Mr Goddard that her nephew's heart was not nearly so bad as he thought it was, and the exercise would do him good. She was, unquestionably, a lady of commanding character.

'He's so full of energy,' said Mrs Dick, watching her husband's progress admiringly. 'I say the air of Ireland has got into his head.'

'Is he not so energetic at home?' asked Mr Goddard.

'Indeed he isn't. Just fancy if he was!'

She giggled convulsively at the thought. It was evident that Mr Dick, though not a Scot, belonged of some part of the country where decorum of demeanour and a certain gravity are expected from Members of Parliament.

'"Fare thee well,"' shouted Mr Dick from the end of the platform, ' "and if for ever, still for ever fare thee well." '

He was wheeling the two bicycles out of the station, and was followed by the obviously reluctant Mr Sanders.

'Richard, Richard!' said his wife.

Mr Dick paused and looked round.

'Have you got your sandwiches? Don't go without your sandwiches. I'm sure they're in my hold-all.'

But Mr Dick patted his coat pocket triumphantly. He had the sandwiches. He was not the kind of man, so his attitude suggested, the feeble and inefficient kind of man, who goes off without his sandwiches. A moment later, having compelled Mr Sanders to mount, he was cycling gaily down the road towards Clonmore.

'Richard, Richard!' shouted his wife again. But it was too late. Her voice did not reach him.

'I'm sure,' she said, turning to Mr Goddard, 'that he doesn't know the way. He has never been here before. He'll get lost. Whatever are we to do?'

Mr Goddard consoled her. He pointed out that Mr Dick had started in the right direction; that it was generally possible to make inquiries when in doubt; that, as a matter of fact, once clear of Clonmore, there was only one road on which anybody could ride a bicycle, and that it led straight to Pool-a-donagh. Miss Farquharson helped to reassure her.

'Where there's a will there's a way,' she said sententiously.

'Do stop him,' said Mrs Dick. 'You must stop him. He's got my pocket-handkerchief in his pocket. I gave it to him to keep for me in the train.'

'I can't,' said Mr Goddard. 'He's gone. He's out of sight. Even if he wasn't, I don't think that I could stop him. But I can lend you a pocket-handkerchief. I have two. This one is quite clean.'

Then came the business of packing the ladies and their belongings on the cars. Mr Goddard, after consultation with the station-master and a porter, gave all the luggage to the driver of Patsy Devlin's grey pony. Jimmy O'Loughlin's mare was the more likely of the two animals to reach Pool-a-donagh, and the station-master pointed out that if there were to be a break down it would be better for the ladies to arrive without their luggage than for the luggage to arrive while the ladies were left on the side of the road. Mrs Dick, recovering her spirits, insisted on carrying out her plan of sitting on the well of the car. There was a small crowd outside the railway station, which watched with reverent wonder her climbing and wriggling. She waved both hands to Mr Goddard as soon as she settled herself comfortably, and was very nearly thrown off the car when the mare started with a jerk. Afterwards she clung to Miss Farquharson and Mrs Sanders, who sat one on each side of her.

It was not until the two cars were well on their way down the road that Mr Goddard recollected the promise he had made to Miss Blow. He had really intended to fulfil it. He had it in his mind to say something of a light and jocular kind about the disappearance of the doctor, something which would redeem the letter of his promise without exciting the Members of Parliament. It was not, he reflected, in any way his fault that he had failed. He had no opportunity of speaking. Mr Dick's impetuous energy had made it quite impossible to approach the subject of Dr O'Grady. But, while his own conscience absolved him, he was quite sure that he would not be able to explain himself satisfactorily to Miss Blow. She would not believe that Members of Parliament could possibly behave as Mr Dick had behaved. She would not understand the effect of the Irish air upon naturally staid men. There was some comfort for him in the thought that the cars, with Mrs Dick's legs swinging off the foremost one, must have passed the hotel, and that Miss Blow might have seen for herself that the party was in no mood for investigating murders. The bicyclists, unless they deliberately turned aside before reaching the town, must also have passed the hotel. Mr Dick very probably sang some song of the open road as he sped through Clonmore. Miss Blow might have heard it, might have seen for herself the sort of people these tourists were. If she did, Mr Goddard's reputation as a man of honour would be safe. She could not possibly expect him to redeem his promise.

Then a fresh and most depressing thought attacked him. The Members of Parliament had come and were gone; but there was another promise of his unfulfilled. Miss Blow would certainly expect him to start at once and search for Dr O'Grady. He knew that he could not postpone the matter any longer. She would pin him to his word, insist upon immediate action, refuse to rest satisfied with excuses. He walked very slowly down the hill from the station.

A cowardly way of escape presented itself to him at the last moment. His horse and trap were in the hotel yard. If he could get them without being seen by Miss Blow he might drive back to Ballymoy. Miss Blow, since the Members of Parliament had got the only available cars, could not follow him. Forgetful of honour and chivalry, of Miss Blow's tear-stained face, of the pressure of her hand, of the kiss which he had nearly given to her glove, he made up his mind to fly. He approached the hotel very cautiously.

Like a thirsty man on a Sunday who has not been able to travel the number of miles which make drinking legal, he climbed over the back wall into the yard. He glanced nervously at the windows, hoping that Miss Blow's room looked out on the front and that she would be expecting him to reach the hotel along the road. He caught sight of Bridgy staring out of the scullery window. She had watched him climb the wall and was most anxious to discover what he intended to do next. It seemed to her unnatural that an officer of police should enter an hotel in such a way. Mr Goddard, taking shelter in the stable, beckoned to her through the door. Filled with curiosity, she crossed the yard and joined him in the stable.

'Bridgy,' he said, 'here's a shilling for you. Is Mr O'Loughlin inside.

'He is, sir,' said Bridgy.

'Then tell him to come out here. I want to speak to him.'

'Is it out to the stable?'

Mr Goddard had sacrificed his own self-respect when he yielded to temptation and made up his mind to escape. He now flung away all hope of ever being respected by Bridgy.

'Yes; here in the stable. And if you meet Miss Blow, don't tell her where I am.'

'I will not. Why would I? But sure——'

'Go on now, like a good girl, and don't waste your time talking to me.'

Jimmy O'Loughlin was a man of tact and good manners. He greeted Mr Goddard cheerfully as if there was nothing surprising in the choice of a stable for the scene of an impor-

tant interview. He had been warned by Bridgy that Mr Goddard, for some reason, stood in terror of Miss Blow; but he
made no allusion to her. He opened the conversation with
a remark on a safe, indifferent topic.

'Them was queer people,' he said, alluding to the Members
of Parliament and their party.

'I want my horse and trap,' said Mr Goddard, 'and I want
to pay my bill. I am going back to Ballymoy at once.'

'I wouldn't say but you're right,' said Jimmy, 'if them ones
is likely to be back here in the course of the day.'

'It's not that. I don't mind about them. It's business that's
taking me home—important business.'

This was too much for Jimmy O'Loughlin. His tact and
manners were good, but was not going to allow Mr Goddard
to escape without an allusion to Miss Blow.

'The doctor's young lady is within, waiting for you,' he said.

'I know that; but I haven't time to talk to her now. In fact,
it is most important that I should get away without her seeing
me—on account of my business.'

'I wouldn't say but you might be right there too,' said
Jimmy.

They set to work together and harnessed Mr Goddard's
horse. They led him into the yard and put him between the
shafts of the trap as silently as possible.

'I'm thinking,' said Jimmy, 'that maybe it would be better
for you not to be paying me the trifle that's due for your bed
and your dinner until the next time you're over.'

'Very well. Then I'll be able to start at once.'

'You will. And, what's more, when the young lady asks me
what's happened to you, I'll be able to say that I don't know
because you went off without paying your bill.'

Jimmy O'Loughlin had a sensitive conscience. He could lie
without hesitation when circumstances required it of him, but
he preferred, where possible, to deceive without departing
from the literal truth.

13

MR DICK, who was a man of energy, rode fast. Mr Sanders toiled behind him, but was able to keep him in sight because Mr Dick dismounted and waited for him at the top of every hill. The day was hot, and there was very little breeze. Neither of the men was in good training. Both of them became thirsty. Five miles outside of Clonmore the road crosses a small river. Mr Dick stopped on the bridge, and, when Mr Sanders overtook him, proposed that they should take a drink. They made their way down to the stream, lay on their stomachs, and sucked up large quantities of luke-warm water. Then they rode on again, and, as might have been expected, became much hotter and thirstier than they were before. Mr Dick stopped again, this time at a pool. Mr Sanders, though very thirsty, expressed doubts about the wholesomeness of the water. Mr Dick explained briefly that, as there was no human habitation in sight, the pool could not possibly be polluted by drains. Then he lay down and drank as eagerly as a camel at an oasis. The pool was shallow, and the violence of his sucking stirred up a good deal of mud. Mr Sanders, realizing that every moment's delay increased the chance of his getting typhoid fever from his draught, chose the cleanest corner of the pool and drank a great deal more than was good for him. The water of the pool was even warmer than that of the river.

Then it was discovered that one of the tyres of the bicycle ridden by Mr Dick had burst. He had pumped it too vehemently, and the heat of the sun had swelled the air inside until the strain was too great for the cover. Both tool-bags were examined, but no materials for repair were found in in them. Even under these circumstances Mr Dick remained cheerful.

'We'll walk on,' he said, 'until we come to a police barrack. We're bound to come to one soon.'

'What good will that be?'

Mr Sanders did not want to walk on if he could help it.

'In Ireland,' said Mr Dick, 'the police are experts at repairing bicycles. One of the people we met last week told me that. He was an inspector of something, and was always going about the country, so he'd be sure to know.'

'In any case,' said Mr Sanders, 'there isn't likely to be a police barrack about here. There are no houses. We haven't passed a single human habitation for the last twenty minutes.'

Mr Dick overruled this objection at once. He had been studying the Irish question for a whole fortnight, and he thoroughly understood the country.

'In Ireland,' he said, 'the most likely place to find a police barrack is where there are no houses. The reason for that is that the uninhabited districts of the country are those from which the people have been evicted. They naturally want to get back again, and so police barracks are built to prevent them doing so. You will always find a barrack where there are no people. A man who was greatly interested in the land question told me that the day before yesterday.'

'I think,' said Mr Sanders, 'that I'll sit down here and wait till the cars overtake me. You can take your own bicycle and go on if you like.'

'You'd better not, because the cars may never overtake you. We may be on the wrong road altogether. I didn't ask the way. I simply steered a course by the sun like an explorer in central Africa.'

'What an ass you are, Dick!'

'Not an ass, Sanders, not an ass, an adventurer. I love risk for its own sake. The blood of the ancient Berserkers is in my veins. I feel like the man in the song "Fiddle and I", that is to say, in this case,

> "Biky and I
> Wandering by
> Over the world together."

If you don't come on with me, Sanders, you will get lost like a babe in the wood, and then

> "When you are dead
> The robins so red
> Will take strawberry leaves and over you spread." '

Mr Sanders shrank from such a fate. Also he had sat down during the discussion and felt rested. He agreed to go on. Mr Dick, the Berserker spirit strong in him, wheeled both bicycles. They climbed a long hill and found walking even hotter work than bicycling. But they had their reward. From the top of the hill the entrance gate and the trees of Rosivera were visible.

'A sail, a sail!' cried Mr Dick. 'We are saved!

> "We shall hear the sweet music of speech
> Nor finish our journey alone." '

'It looks like a gentleman's place,' said Mr Sanders, 'a dilapidated gentleman's place. I mean to say, of course, the dilapidated place of a gentleman.'

Mr Dick was not a stickler for the nice arrangement of adjectives.

'Of course,' he said, 'it's a dilapidated gentleman's place. All gentlemen's places in Ireland are dilapidated. That is one of the consequences of the recent land legislation.'

'Rents,' said Mr Sanders, who took a special delight in all kinds of figures, 'were reduced twenty per cent. all round on an average at first fixing. Then they were reduced again by——'

'Come on,' said Mr Dick. 'The proprietor, whoever he is,

must have enough left to buy a repair outfit. Let's go and borrow it.'

He had heard quite as much as he wanted to hear about rent fixing and land purchase during the fortnight he had spent in Ireland. He did not want to go into the matter again. It required intricate calculations, and Mr Dick had no taste for arithmetic. Mr Sanders sighed and followed his friend down the hill.

They passed through the gate of Rosivera and went down the avenue, Mr Dick leading the way with the two bicycles. Turning a corner, they came suddenly upon a view of the house. Beyond it, at the bottom of the lawn, lay the bay.

'Dilapidated!' said Mr Sanders, in disgust. 'I knew it would be dilapidated, but I didn't expect it to be as bad as this. It looks to me as if it were uninhabited.'

Mr Dick paid no attention to the appearance of the house. The sight of the sea seemed to intoxicate him. He was very hot and very dusty. The idea of bathing in cold water was delightful.

'We'll have a swim,' he said. 'First we'll knock up the proprietor, borrow the repair outfit, and mend the tyre. Then we'll go round the corner, out of sight of the house, and wallow in the briny wave.'

But Mr Sanders was cautious, more cautious than he had been about drinking the water out of the pool.

'You've no towel,' he said.

'What do we care for towels? We are primitive men, savages on our native wild, cave dwellers of the paleolithic age. I should spurn a towel if it was offered me.'

'That's all very well for you, Dick; but I have a weak heart, and I have to be careful. In the heated state in which I am at present, I daren't risk bathing, especially without a towel.'

'Then I'll bathe by myself. You can get the bicycle repaired. By the time you have it settled I shall be ready to start again.'

They reached the house. Mr Dick commented, laughing, on the fact that there was no electric bell. Mr Sanders sighed at this fresh evidence of dilapidation. There was no knocker either. Mr Dick hammered on the door with his fist until he thought he had made noise enough to attract attention. Then he walked on towards the shore, leaving his friend alone to enjoy the hospitality or face the wrath of the inmates of the house. Mr Sanders waited for some time and then knocked again. After another pause he tried kicking the door. Then he rang both the bicycle bells. At last he began to despair of attracting attention. Some men, under the circumstances, would have gone away. Mr Sanders was persevering and little troubled with delicacy of feeling. He pushed open the door and walked in.

Mr Dick, yearning for a swim, soon found a spot which seemed sufficiently secluded. It was not particularly attractive as a bathing-place. The beach was covered with small rough stones; and, the tide being out, there was a considerable stretch of beach. The water near the shore was full of jellyfish and brown seaweed. But Mr Dick was too hot and too eager to care much about these inconveniences. His desire was to get as quickly as possible into the sea. He undressed beside a large stone which lay just above high-water mark. Then his troubles began. He had never before walked on such trying stones. The pain which they gave his feet caused him to stumble and fall suddenly forward on his hands. Part of the journey he accomplished on all-fours. The seaweed was a relief when he reached it. The jellyfish were deliciously soft under his feet. He floundered out through them and over them until the water reached his knees. Then he flung himself forward and struck out. The weed brushed his limbs and body. The jellyfish, incredible numbers of them, slipped past him.

'This,' he said, 'is delicious.'

He got past the belt of weed and jellyfish into deep water. He shouted aloud in his joy—a wild inarticulate whoop which went sounding across the waters of the bay. He lay on his back. He kicked with his legs, raised what seemed to him splendid fountains of water. He shouted again. Then he swam further out, using a side stroke which he had learned in a swimming-bath, burying his head each time his arm left the water, and then turning his face up and snorting like a porpoise. After awhile he lay on his back again and began to sing—

'Rule, Britannia! Britannia rules the waves.'

The ditty was appropriate enough. Mr Dick M.P., represented in Rosivera Bay the world's greatest maritime power, and he had, plainly, so far got the better of the sea that it was obliged to bear him on his breast and minister to his delight. He ruled it. There were, indeed, no waves; but that was not Mr Dick's fault. If there had been waves, he would have ruled them.

'Rule, Britannia!' he sang again, 'Britannia rules the waves. Britons never, never, never shall be slaves.'

Mr Dick had a poor ear for music, and his rendering of the tune was far from correct; but he had a fine voice and it rang out satisfactorily. He felt more than ever like an ancient Berserker. His song was a kind of triumphant challenge to man and nature alike.

'This,' he said breathlessly, when he had finished the song for the third time, 'is better than mending bicycles. I wonder how poor Sanders is getting on?'

He wallowed round and faced the shore. He saw a man approaching from the direction in which the house lay.

'Hullo—lo—o!' he shouted. 'Coo—ee, Sanders!'

Then he saw that it was not Mr Sanders. He came to the conclusion that it must be one of the inhabitants of the house. He was perfectly right. It was Mr Red.

'Funny-looking old cock he is,' said Mr Dick.

Mr Red stalked majestically along the shore. Mr Dick swam to meet him. His heart was light. He broke into a song of greeting—

'Come o'er the sea,
Stranger to me,
Mine through sunshine, storm and cloud!'

Mr Red walked straight to the place where Mr Dick's
clothes lay. It seemed possible that he was bringing down a
towel. Mr Dick swam on towards the shore, intending to express his gratitude for the civility. Mr Red reached the clothes,
picked them up one by one and walked away with them. Mr
Dick shouted after him, but without effect. He swam for the
shore as quickly as he could. If the proprietor of the place objected to people bathing on the shore, Mr Dick was prepared
to apologize. He would apologize humbly, get back his
clothes, and then point out that a notice ought to have been
erected to warn the public not to bathe. Mr Red deposited the
clothes on the grass at some distance from the beach, turned
round, and walked towards the sea again. Mr Dick felt bottom with his feet, and plunged forward until he stood in water
which only reached to his knees. Mr Red, standing on the very
brink of the sea, took a revolver out of his pocket and pointed
it at Mr Dick.

'Come on shore,' he said.

By way of reply Mr Dick sat down suddenly, rolled over
on his side, and lay with no part of him above water except his
head. He did not like standing naked in front of a revolver
which might be loaded.

'Come!' said Mr Red.

Mr Dick put his head under water, and kept it there as long
as he could. When he came up, gasping, he saw the revolver
still levelled at him.

'Come at once,' said Mr Red, 'or I shall fire!'

Mr Dick struggled to his feet and stumbled forward a few
steps. Then his self-respect, the self-respect which is the birth-
right of every free-born Briton, asserted itself within him.

'I presume,' he said, speaking with a certain cold dignity,
'that this beach is private property, and that I have trespassed

133

by bathing here. If so, I offer my apologies; but I cannot re-frain from saying at the same time that the aggressive violence of your conduct——'

Mr Red pulled the trigger of the revolver. A bullet struck the water so close to Mr Dick that his leg was splashed. He stopped short in his protest and waded as rapidly as possible towards the shore. He pushed his way through the seaweed and jellyfish and stood at last, a pitiful dripping figure, on dry land.

'Go on,' said Mr Red, fingering the revolver.

The fear of instant death impelled Mr Dick over the sharp stones. He travelled rapidly for five or six yards, and then collapsed suddenly on to all-fours.

'Go on quickly,' said Mr Red.

Mr Dick went on as quickly as he could on his hands and feet. He looked like a large hairless ape of some bleached kind. Then, overcome by the pain of both hands and feet, he sat down and faced Mr Red.

'This is an outrage,' he said. 'I protest against it in the strongest possible manner. You have absolutely no right——'

'Get up,' said Mr Red, 'and precede me to the house.'

Mr Dick got up with a groan. He was really suffering con-siderably. The Berserker spirit, active in him during an earlier part of the day, was almost dead. He staggered on a few steps. Then a new notion seized him, a fear which was actually stronger than the fear of death. He understood suddenly that he was not, as he had boasted, a primitive man; that he was, on the contrary, highly civilized. He turned on Mr Red and faced the revolver without a tremor.

'I won't go to the house without my clothes,' he said. 'There may be ladies. There may be servants.'

There was a determination in the way he spoke and in the expression of his face which was quite unmistakable. Mr Red tried to bully him, but failed. No threat was of any avail.

'I won't go,' said Mr Dick, 'unless I can have my shirt at least.'

'You can have your shirt,' said Mr Red. 'Go and get it.'

Mr Dick made his way slowly across the beach. He looked over his shoulder from time to time, and saw that Mr Red was following closely with the revolver. He reached the grass, felt it soft under his feet, and moved more easily. It occurred to him that he might make a dash for liberty. Mr Red would shoot, no doubt; but he might miss. He might hit, and still only wound—wound in some trifling way which would not prevent further flight. There was a grove of trees not fifty yards distant. They were small, scrubby trees, but they would afford some shelter. He made up his mind to risk it. Then the awful prospect before him made him pause. How could he—even supposing that he was not shot dead at once—wander stark naked through a strange country?

He reached the pile of clothes, stooped down and picked up his shirt. Then he took up his trousers.

'Drop that,' said Mr Red.

Dean Swift noted the fact that an unarmed man in his shirt is likely to get the worst of a struggle with eight armed men who are fully dressed. The chances are more equal, if there is only one armed man, if the unarmed man gets his trousers on. Mr Red knew this, and strictly limited Mr Dick's clothing. He was not prepared to run any unnecessary risk with his prisoner. The warmth of the shirt, which was flannel, restored Mr Dick's self-respect and courage. He turned on Mr Red once more.

'If this is the way that Irish landlords habitually behave,' he said, 'I don't wonder that there has been an agrarian revolution in the country. I always had a certain sympathy with your class before, but now that I know what you really are I shall vote for the next Land Bill that is brought in, whatever it is.'

'Precede me to the house,' said Mr Red.

Mr Dick walked on. He crossed the grass rapidly and came to the gravel sweep in front of the house. Here his feet began to give him great pain again. The gravel was in some ways worse than the stones on the beach had been. Mr Dick felt it severely.

'I've heard stories,' said Mr Dick, 'of the way you Irish landlords treated your tenants in the past. I know now that I didn't hear half the truth. Anything more abominable, more outrageous, more utterly illegal——'

He reached the door of the house as he spoke, and stepped with a sigh of relief on to the smooth step.

'Look here,' he said, 'where's Sanders? Have you murdered Sanders?'

He went forward again, passed through the door, and stood in the hall.

There, in front of him, bound hand and foot, guarded by the long-bearded anarchist, lay Mr Sanders.

14

MR RED treated Dr O'Grady and Patsy Devlin very well. They could not have fared better if they had been political prisoners awaiting a trial for inciting people to boycott each other. They had abundance of excellent food, three meals a day, brought up to them by one of the foreign anarchists. They had a sufficiency of whisky and tobacco. A second bed was supplied when the doctor objected to sleeping with Patsy Devlin. Twice every day Dr O'Grady was taken downstairs and allowed to attend the injured man, who was recovering rapidly. Every evening Mr Red, adhering honourably to his bargain, handed over five sovereigns to the doctor. A large number of books was supplied to the prisoners. They were chiefly treatises on the theory and practice of anarchism, accounts of the revolution in Russia, and kindred matters. Dr O'Grady was perfectly content with them. The subject was new to him, and he read with excited curiosity. It was a favourite boast of his that no book of any kind bored him, provided that he understood the language in which it was written. Unfortunately, Patsy Devlin did not like reading. He worked slowly through the accounts of the murders of a few Grand Dukes, and displayed some slight interest in the tortures inflicted on a female anarchist. Then he became bored and refused to read any more. He used to walk about the room whistling loudly. There were only two tunes which he cared to whistle—'The wearing of the Green' and 'God save Ireland'. The constant repetition of them began to irritate Dr O'Grady at the end of the second day of Patsy's captivity. He expostulated, and Patsy agreed to stop whistling. He was a man of kindly heart and had a real affection for the doctor.

'I wouldn't,' he said, 'be doing what might annoy you; and if so be that the tunes is disagreeable, there won't be another note of them heard from this out.'

He meant what he said, but he promised more than he was able to perform. It soon appeared that he could not help whistling. He did not, in fact, know when he was whistling. The tunes came bubbling from his pursed lips against his will.

Dr O'Grady recognized that Patsy could not accomplish the impossible. He gave up reading about anarchists, and asked Mr Red for a pack of cards. The request, a reasonable one, was refused, and Dr O'Grady snubbed for making it. Mr Red disapproved of card-playing on principle. He said that games of chance were demoralising to the human race. As a consistent anarchist he could not and would not allow them to be played in his house. Then Dr O'Grady invented a game which could be played with coins on a table. A penny was placed at a short distance from the edge of the table and driven along by the impact of another penny flipped at it from the edge.

The object was to hit the first penny as frequently as possible before it was driven over the opposite edge of the table. Patsy displayed a great aptitude for the game. After an hour's play he was fairly expert. Before the end of the afternoon he had won ninepence from Dr O'Grady. He practised assiduously next morning while the doctor read anarchist books. During the afternoon and evening he won, to his great delight, sums which amounted altogether to one-and-sevenpence. He did not whistle while he practised or played. In order to concentrate his whole energy on the game he was obliged to keep his mouth wide open.

A game was in full swing on the third afternoon of Patsy's captivity when the key turned in the lock and the door of the room was flung open.

'Now what,' said Dr O'Grady, 'can the Emperor possibly want with us at this hour of the day? It's not tea-time.'

Mr Dick, clad only in his grey flannel shirt, walked in.

'Hallo!' said Dr O'Grady, 'are you an anti-military anarchist getting into training for the simple life? Or are you a new recruit undergoing the ceremony of initiation into the brotherhood? Or is it nothing but the heat of the day?'

Mr Red and the bearded anarchist dragged Mr Sanders into the room and deposited him, still bound, on the floor.

'Oh,' said the doctor, 'another captive! Good. But don't overdo the thing, Emperor. You can't you know, go on storing up men in this way without attracting public attention. Patsy Devlin and I are all right, of course. We're not important people. Nobody misses us in the least. But that man on the floor looks to me like a commercial traveller, and if he happens to belong to any English firm, a search will be made sooner or later for him.'

'We are Members of Parliament,' said Mr Dick.

'You don't look as if you were,' said the doctor. 'Does he, Patsy?'

'Be damn, but he does not! I've seen some queer fellows made Members of Parliament in my day. There was one time

138

I was very near going in for it myself; but I never heard tell of e'er a one yet but owned a pair of breeches—to start with, anyway.'

'You hear what Patsy Devlin says,' said the doctor. 'He quite agrees with me that you don't look like a Member of Parliament.'

Mr Red, with his assistant anarchist, left the room and locked the door behind him. Dr O'Grady shouted after him.

'Hullo! Emperor! I say, are you there? Wait a minute before you go away. Are you listening to me?'

'I hear.'

Mr Red's voice, coming through the shut door, sounded more solemn than usual.

'I'm glad you do,' said Dr O'Grady. 'Don't go away now till I've finished speaking. I want you to understand that we can't possibly have these two fellows billeted here on us. It's all very fine for you to go about picking up all sorts of people off the public roads and dumping them down here; but Patsy Devlin and I don't like it. It's not fair. I told you before that we don't in the least object to be imprisoned; but we bar having an escaped lunatic with nothing on but a shirt, and a wretched commercial traveller shoved in here into a room which we have come to regard as our private apartment.'

'We are Members of Parliament,' said Mr Dick. 'We demand to be taken at once before the British Consul.'

He appeared to think, not at all unnaturally, that he had strayed beyond the bounds of His Majesty's dominions.

'Do shut up,' said Dr O'Grady, in a whisper. 'We don't believe you're Members of Parliament. Nor does the Emperor. As a matter of fact, you're not up to the level of the average county councillor in the way of respectability. Saying absurd things like that will simply enrage the Emperor. He's frightfully touchy, and the moment he loses his temper he shoots off his pistol. I say,' he went on in a loud tone, 'are you there still? Hang it, I believe he's gone. That's your fault.' He addressed Mr Dick. 'Why didn't you keep your mouth shut and let me talk to him? Now the Emperor won't be back till tea-time, and we'll have to put up with you till then. Perhaps, as you are here, you'll kindly explain what you mean by bursting in on us unannounced in this way. You might at least have knocked at the door.'

'I was bathing——' began Mr Dick.

'Where?'

'I don't know. Just outside the house. He came and took away my clothes.'

'Serves you jolly well right,' said the doctor. 'What made you come here, of all places in the world, to bathe? Surely to goodness the Atlantic Ocean is big enough to bathe in without your picking out the exact spot in which the Anti-Military Anarchists are maturing their plans. Why did you do it?'

'Anarchists?'

'Yes, Anti-Military Anarchists—the very worst sort there is.'

'I thought he was a landlord.'

'Well, he isn't. He's as nearly as possible the exact reverse.'

'Are you an anarchist too?'

'No, I'm not,' said Dr O'Grady, 'nor is Patsy Devlin. So far we haven't been asked to join the organisation. We're simply prisoners. We've been captured by the brotherhood. But we had sense enough to wear our ordinary clothes. You may think it's the proper thing to go about in nothing but your shirt because you happen to be in the house of an anarchist, but I can tell you——'

Mr Sanders, who still lay on the floor, groaned dismally.

'Loose that fellow, Patsy,' said the doctor. 'He appears to be in pain of some sort.'

'Anarchists!' said Mr Dick. 'Good heavens! How frightful! My wife! My poor wife!'

'She'll be all right,' said the doctor. 'The Emperor won't do her any harm. He's a thorough gentleman in every way, a chivalrous gentleman, and I'm perfectly certain he wouldn't ill-treat a woman. You may rely on it that she'll be made quite comfortable. She was with you, I suppose. If so, I don't in the least wonder that you were run in. The Emperor has frightfully strict, old-fashioned ideas about lots of things. He objects to cards, for instance, as demoralising. I'm sure that mixed bathing would simply horrify him. There's no greater mistake than to think that just because a man's an anarchist you can do what you like without shocking him. You can't. The Emperor has his prejudices just like the rest of us.'

Patsy Devlin set Mr Sanders on his feet and rubbed him down carefully. The poor man seemed dazed and bewildered.

'Do you belong to the bathing party too?' asked Dr O'Grady. 'Or are you a separate and distinct capture, unconnected with the gentleman in the flannel shirt?'

'I don't bathe,' said Mr Sanders, 'because I have a weak heart and it doesn't agree with me.'

'Then what were you doing? You must have been doing something which annoyed the Emperor. He may be a bit touched in the head. Most of us are, more or less; but he's not so mad as to saddle himself with the expense of boarding and lodging a fellow like you unless you have been doing something he dislikes. What were you at?'

'I was mending a bicycle, Mrs Dick's bicycle; at least——'

'Who is Mrs Dick?' said Dr O'Grady. 'The lady who was bathing?'

'She wasn't bathing,' said Mr Dick.

'All right. Don't get angry. I thought your name might be Dick and that the lady might be your wife.'

'My name is Dick, and she is my wife.'

'I don't understand you in the least,' said Dr O'Grady. 'Have you got two wives? Has that anything to do with the way you're going about with nothing on but your shirt?'

'No, it hasn't; and I've not got two wives.'

'You must have two wives,' said Dr O'Grady. 'You told me this instant that your wife was bathing with you on the shore. And now you say Mrs Dick wasn't bathing. Those two statements can't possibly both be true about the same woman. But I won't go into that yet. Later on you shall have an opportunity of clearing yourself if you can. First of all, I want to get to the bottom of this bicycle business, which seems to be less complicated.'

He turned to Mr Sanders. 'You say that you were engaged in mending Mrs Dick's bicycle when the Emperor came on you.'

'Yes,' said Mr Sanders. 'At least I wanted to mend it.'

'That's not exactly the same thing. I wish you'd try to be accurate. There's no use my attempting to unravel this tangle and get at the truth for you if you won't be careful what you say. Go on.'

'I knocked for some time at the door, but nobody came to me. Then I——'

'I expect,' said the doctor, 'that the Emperor was in the Chamber of Research at the time, concocting some new kind of dynamite. That's his favourite occupation.'

'Good God!' said Mr Sanders.

'It's all right. Don't be afraid. The mixtures he makes hardly ever go off. And in any case he won't want to blow you up unless you are a soldier. You're not in the army, are you? You don't look as if you were.'

'No.'

'Or in the militia? The Emperor has a perfect horror of militiamen. Hasn't he, Patsy?'

'He damn nearly shot me,' said Patsy, 'when I told him I'd been in the militia.'

'Let's get back to the bicycle,' said Dr O'Grady. 'Mrs Dick's bicycle, as I understand, which you wanted to mend. When you found that nobody took any notice of your knocking, what did you do?'

'I pushed the door open—it wasn't locked or bolted—and stepped in.'

'That strikes me,' said Dr O'Grady, 'as pretty fair cheek on your part, considering that you're not an Anti-Military Anarchist. You might have guessed that it would irritate the

Emperor, especially as he was making dynamite at the time. What happened next?'

'I looked round and saw no one. I rang the dinner gong, which was standing in a corner of the hall. When that didn't attract anybody's attention I tried the door on the right, and found it locked.'

'It's a pity you didn't try the one on the left. If you had, you'd have seen the yellow crocodiles, and they'd have frightened you out of the house.'

'Then, just as I was turning to go away, two men sprang on me and bound me. After that I knew no more until——'

'I wish,' said Mr Dick, interrupting his friend's story, 'that somebody would lend me a pair of trousers.'

'I haven't got any spare trousers,' said Dr O'Grady, 'and if I had, I'm not at all sure that I'd lend them to you. You say you're a Member of Parliament; but I've no proof of that. And even if you are it doesn't seem to me to follow that you'd return the trousers.'

'What am I to do?' said Mr Dick. 'I can't go about in this state all day.'

'You won't go about much in any case,' said the doctor. 'But for the immediate present I think you'd better get into Patsy Devlin's bed. It's no pleasure to us to see you standing about in your shirt. When you're in bed I shall ask you a few questions, and if it turns out that the Emperor really has got your clothes, I'll do my best to persuade him to give them back to you when he comes up here at tea-time. I suppose you don't mind his getting into your bed, Patsy, just for the present?'

'I do not,' said Patsy, 'as long as he's out of it before I'm wanting it myself.'

Mr Dick crept in between the blankets.

'Now,' said the doctor, 'we'll take up your story. You have, as I understand, two wives, one of whom bathes, and the other owns a bicycle.'

Mr Dick sat up and protested strongly. He appealed to Mr Sanders to clear him of the charge of bigamy.

'All right,' said Dr O'Grady; 'I'll accept the statement that you've only one. Was she, or was she not, bathing with you when the Emperor came on you? Be careful how you answer.'

'Certainly not. She's—I trust she's miles away, and safe.'

'Then why did you express anxiety about the way the Emperor was likely to treat her?'

'I didn't.'

'You did. You kept saying, "My poor wife." What did you mean by that, if you didn't mean that the Emperor had captured her?'

'I meant that she'd be anxious about me.'

'She can't be as fond of you as all that,' said the doctor. 'Nobody could.'

'She's very fond of me. We're only quite lately married.'

'Have you a wife too?' said the doctor to Mr Sanders.

'Yes. I have a wife and an aunt. They're both with me in Ireland.'

'Do you suppose that your wife is as fond of you as Mrs Dick is of her husband?'

'I don't know. How could I know that?'

'The reason I ask the question,' said Dr O'Grady, 'is this. There's a girl I'm engaged to be married to, a Miss Adeline Maud Blow, who is probably scouring the country in pursuit of me this minute. Patsy Devlin has a wife who may be out looking for him.'

'The minute she'd find out I was gone,' said Patsy, 'she'd be up at the barrack telling the police, the way she'd have me brought back to her.'

'And now,' said the doctor, 'it turns out that Mr Dick has a wife, or perhaps two, of an unusually affectionate kind. And you have a wife and an aunt who have some regard for you. That makes five women altogether, all of them more or less energetic, and all of them bent on finding us. The question is, how long will it be before they think of coming to Rosivera?'

'Not long,' said Mr Sanders, 'not long, I hope.'

'For the sake of my poor wife,' said Mr Dick, who had covered himself with the bed-clothes again, 'I trust it will not be long.'

'Be damn,' said Patsy Devlin, 'but to listen to the way you're talking, a man would think nobody in the world but yourself ever had a wife. I have one myself, as the doctor was saying this minute, and I wouldn't wonder but she might be a better one than yours. But you don't hear me lamenting over her every time I open my mouth.'

'Tell me this,' said the doctor: 'did you ever escape from your wife before?'

'Escape from her!'

'I mean, did you ever temporarily desert her, either through being taken prisoner or otherwise?'

'Never,' said Mr Dick. 'We've only been a year married, and we've never been parted, even for a single day.'

'That's all right,' said the doctor. 'Then she won't have had any practice in looking for you. Patsy Devlin's wife, as you heard, is likely to go straight to the police barrack when she misses him. But then she's more or less accustomed to his not turning up regularly.'

'I wouldn't say,' said Patsy, 'that the police would be paying too much attention to what she might tell them.'

'What about your wife, and your aunt?' said the doctor to Mr Sanders. 'Are they accustomed to having to hunt you up?'

'Do I gather from what you say,' said Mr Sanders, 'that you don't want to be rescued?'

'We certainly do not,' said the doctor. 'Patsy and I are perfectly comfortable where we are. We know when we are well off.'

'Good God!' said Mr Sanders. 'In the hands of a bloodthirsty anarchist!'

'Don't abuse the Emperor,' said the doctor, 'for I won't

stand it. He may be an anarchist, but he's a thoroughly good sort.'

'I'm thankful to say,' said Mr Sanders, 'that my aunt is a woman of great vigour and determination. She will do everything that can be done to discover where we are and to rescue us. I place implicit confidence in her. Nothing will daunt her.'

'If, as I gather from your description of her, she is any kind of Suffragette,' said the doctor, 'I hope, for her own sake, that she'll keep clear of the Emperor. He has the strongest possible prejudice against advanced women. I happened one day to mention the name of Jael to him in the course of conversation. You know the woman I mean, the one who hammered the nail into the man's head. I naturally thought he'd admire her immensely, but he didn't in the least. He flew into the most frightful rage. Didn't he, Patsy?'

'I heard you saying so,' said Patsy, 'and of course I believed you. But I wasn't here myself at the time. You know that, doctor.'

Mr Sanders brightened up suddenly.

'Are you a doctor?' he said.

'I am, or I was, the dispensary doctor of Clonmore Poor Law Union. By the way, Patsy, was there any talk of their electing a new man when they found out that I'd gone?'

'I wouldn't be telling you a lie. There was.'

'If you're a doctor,' said Mr Sanders eagerly, 'you'll be able to certify that I have a weak heart, and that confinement will seriously injure my health. Then he'll be bound to let me go.'

'I haven't a stethoscope with me,' said the doctor, 'so I can't. But even if I wrote you out quite a long certificate I don't suppose that it would influence the Emperor in the least. He doesn't care about your health. Why should he?'

'But I've always understood—— Why, the Home Secretary only the other day——'

'And I may as well tell you straight,' said the doctor, 'that if I had a stethoscope, and if the Emperor would let you out on my certificate, I wouldn't give it. In fact, if I certified at all,

I'd certify that you are a particularly strong and enduring kind of man, and that a little imprisonment would do you good.'

'But why——? Why should——?'

'Because the first thing you'd do when you got out would be to bring the police down on us here, and that's exactly what we don't want.'

15

MISS BLOW stood at the window of her bedroom in Jimmy O'Loughlin's hotel, and saw Mr Dick and Mr Sanders ride by on their bicycles. She did not for a moment suppose that they were the Members of Parliament who had arrived by the train. They looked like hilarious but shabby tourists. It is not with such faces or in such clothes that candidates for election woo their constituents in Merrie England. She afterwards saw the three ladies drive by, followed by the car which carried their luggage. She did not see Mr Goddard. She supposed, very naturally, that he and the Members of Parliament were consulting together somewhere, perhaps in the waiting-room at the railway station, devising plans for the rescue of what still might remain of Dr O'Grady's body. She waited patiently, sustained by the hope of heroic measures to be taken in the near future.

At half-past one Bridgy knocked at the door, and told her that her dinner was ready for her.

'Will Mr Goddard be in for dinner?' asked Miss Blow.

Bridgy did not feel that it was her duty to disclose the fact that Mr Goddard had driven away in the direction of Bally-moy. She answered cautiously.

'He might,' she said.

This was unquestionably true. It was possible that Mr Goddard would repent as he went on his way, and come back to dine with Miss Blow. It was not, in Bridgy's opinion, at all likely that he would; but she did not say this to Miss Blow.

'Will the other gentlemen be with him?'

'Well, I don't know, miss.'

She did know, but she held charity to be a higher virtue than truth. If Miss Blow hoped for the company of other gentlemen, Bridgy would not subject her to a disappointment sooner than was absolutely necessary.

Miss Blow dined alone. After dinner she waited another half-hour. Then she rang the bell for Bridgy.

'Has Mr Goddard come back yet?'

'Well, I don't know, miss.'

'Are the other gentlemen in the hotel?'

'Well, I don't know.'

'Go and find out, then,' said Miss Blow.

Bridgy went downstairs and summoned Jimmy O'Loughlin from behind the bar.

'The young lady above,' she said, 'is asking me this two hours if Mr Goddard is come back.'

'You know as well as I do,' said Jimmy, 'that he hasn't, and, what's more, won't.'

'Sure, I do know that. Didn't I see him making off out of the yard by the back gate the way she wouldn't see him go?'

'Well, then, go and tell her so.'

'Is it me? I dursn't.'

'Do it at once,' said Jimmy. 'It was you she asked, and it's you that ought to answer her. Off with you now, and not another word out of your head.'

Bridgy, who saw no reason why she should face the wrath of Miss Blow, retired to a small room which opened off the scullery, and spent an hour cleaning her own boots. Miss Blow

148

waited, and after a while got tired of waiting. She rang the bell again. Bridgy heard it, and, for greater security, went into the yard and concealed herself in the cow byre. Miss Blow came downstairs and found Jimmy O'Loughlin. He had not thought of hiding, and was caught unawares.

'Is Mr Goddard in the hotel?' she asked.

'He is not,' said Jimmy. 'It's himself was sorry to go; but there came a messenger over from Ballymoy, a police sergeant, to say he was wanting, and wanting badly. It might be cattle driving that's in it, or it might be a meeting about the land or maybe an eviction. They're a queer lot down in them parts. Anyway, he was wanting, and he went.'

'It's a curious thing,' said Miss Blow, 'that he went off without saying a word to me.'

'Well, now,' said Jimmy, 'if I amn't the fool this day; but I thought Bridgy would be sure to tell you.'

'Tell me what?'

'The last words he said to me as he was getting up into the trap was these; "Jimmy," says he, "it goes to my heart to be leaving Miss Blow behind me, and her in trouble. She'll never forgive me." "Believe you me," says I, striving to encourage him, for I could see he felt it, "she will." "She will not," says he. "Don't I know she won't?" "She will," says I. "There isn't a young lady ever I met with a better heart." "Will you tell her," says he, "that it was forced on me or I wouldn't do it, not if you was to give me the full of my hat of golden sovereigns?" "I'll tell her," says I; "I'll break it to her quiet and easy the way she won't be feeling it." And, glory be to God, I have.'

'You might have done it a little sooner,' said Miss Blow.

'I might, and that's a fact,' said Jimmy apologetically.

'Where are the other gentlemen?' said Miss Blow.

'The other gentlemen! Is it them ones that come in on the train? Did you not see them going by on their bicycles? They're the most of the way to Pool-a-donagh by this time.'

It occurred to Miss Blow that she had been deceived, tricked, abominably insulted by Mr Goddard. She distinctly remembered the bicyclists. They had passed down the street almost immediately after the arrival of the train. It was quite impossible for Mr Goddard to have had any serious conversation with them. She hesitated, on the verge of tears. Then the utter futility of weeping in the presence of Jimmy O'Loughlin struck her. She pulled herself together and, with prompt decision, settled her course of action.

'Get the car,' she said, 'at once. I shall drive over to Ballymoy and see Mr Goddard.'

'The car's not in it,' said Jimmy.

Miss Blow stamped her foot.

'Get any car,' she said. 'I don't care whether it's your own or another.'

'Divil the car there is in Clonmore this minute,' said Jimmy. 'The ladies that come in by the train has the both of them took, and they're away off with them to Pool-a-donagh, if so be that the horses can do the journey.'

'Do you mean to say that there isn't a horse and car to be got in the place?'

'There is not. It's the truth I'm telling you; and if you don't believe me, go up and ask Sergeant Farrelly at the barrack.'

'Then,' said Miss Blow, 'I'll walk.'

'Is it to walk to Ballymoy? You'd never over it, and the weather as hot as it is. It's better than twelve miles.'

'I'll do it,' said Miss Blow.

She did. A little footsore, very tired, but still blazing with indignation, she arrived in Ballymoy at a quarter to six o'clock.

Just outside Ballymoy, close to the Clonmore road, is the ground belonging to the tennis club. There are three courts and a galvanized iron hut, known as the pavilion. On club days, when some lady gives tea to the players, there are usually twenty or thirty people on the ground. On other days only a few enthusiasts go to the club. It happened that when Miss Blow came in sight on the road there was no one at the club except Mr Goddard and Captain Fielding, the Resident

Magistrate. They were playing a vigorous game, having a final practice in preparation for the tournament which was to be held next day. Mr Goddard was serving in the fifth game of the set when he caught sight of Miss Blow. He paused, stared at her, dropped the two balls which he held in his hand, and fled without a word into the pavilion.

Captain Fielding gaped with astonishment, looked up and down the road, saw nothing very alarming, and followed Mr Goddard into the pavilion.

'What the devil——' he began.

Mr Goddard took no notice of the remark. He was staring out of a small window which commanded a view of the road.

'What the——' said Captain Fielding again.

Mr Goddard turned suddenly.

'Fielding,' he said, 'jump on your bicycle and ride like hell to my house. Don't lose a moment. Get a hold of my housekeeper, and tell her that if any lady calls she's to say I've gone away on leave and won't be back for six weeks. Don't stop to ask questions. I'll explain it all to you when you get back.'

He pushed Captain Fielding out of the pavilion.

'You'll be in time,' he said, 'if only you'll go. Thank goodness my house is at the far end of the town.'

Captain Fielding did as he was told. He rode fast, because he was most anxious to hear Mr Goddard's explanation as soon as posible. He delivered his message to the housekeeper, and then rode back.

'Did you pass a girl walking along the road?' said Mr Goddard.

'I did; a pretty girl in a grey dress, a stranger.'

'Well, she's mad—stark mad. She's been bothering me out of my life these two days. I'm sick and tired of talking to her. If she catches me now I'm done.'

'If she's mad,' said the R.M., 'why don't you have her locked up? I'll sign the papers for you if you get a medical certificate.'

'She's not mad in that sort of way', said Goddard, 'although she is mad.'

'I see,' said the R. M.; 'temper. It's not a breach of promise case, is it, Goddard?'

'Nothing of the sort. I never set eyes on her in my life till yesterday. In fact, she's engaged to quite another man.'

'I see,' said the R. M. doubtfully.

'The fact is,' said Goddard, 'she has a theory that there has been a murder over at Clonmore. There hasn't, of course; but she thinks there has—and—well, the fact is, I promised to investigate it. She cried, you know, and that sort of thing. The whole business is utterly absurd from start to finish.'

'And what do you propose to do now?'

'I don't know. Perhaps she'll go away when she gets the message about my being on leave. I shall stay here till after dark, anyhow, and then sneak down to the house and find out what's happened.'

'I think,' said Captain Fielding, 'that I'll stay with you. I'd rather like to see this business through. Besides, when she finds she can't get you she'll probably go up to my house for me.'

Miss Blow received the message from Mr Goddard's housekeeper with open incredulity.

'I shall wait here,' she said, 'until Mr Goddard comes home.'

The servant was in a difficult position. She recognized Miss Blow as the lady to whom she had given tea the day before, who had driven off, apparently on the most friendly terms, with Mr Goddard. It was plainly impossible to slam the door as doors are slammed in the faces of drunken tramps. She was a woman of kindly disposition. She saw that Miss Blow was dusty, tired, in need of rest and refreshment. Her natural impulse was to be hospitable. At the same time she had no doubt as to what Mr Goddard's wishes were with regard to this particular visitor. She was a woman of intelligence, and she realized that the message delivered by Captain Fielding was urgent and important. She hesitated, standing in the middle of the doorway. Miss Blow put an end to all uncertainty by walking past her into the house, opening the dining-room door, entering the room, and sitting down.

Mr Goddard's housekeeper retired to the kitchen and meditated on the situation. It was plainly impossible to remove Miss Blow without the use of actual force. At seven o'clock pity triumphed over her sense of duty to her master. She made some tea and took it in to Miss Blow on a tray. At eight o'clock a police constable came to the door and asked to see Mr Goddard. He refused to believe that the District inspector had gone on leave. The housekeeper, despairing of anything except the actual truth, confessed that there was a young lady in the house, and gave it as her opinion that Mr Goddard was afraid to meet her. The constable disappeared, grinning. The housekeeper was uneasily conscious that he was putting a wrong meaning into the fact of Miss Blow's presence in the house.

At nine o'clock Mr Goddard, still in tennis flannels, and accompanied by Captain Fielding, climbed over the wall of his back garden, and slipped through the yard into the kitchen.

'Mary,' he said to the housekeeper, 'is that young lady gone?'

'She is not; and, what's more, it's my opinion that she won't go.'

'There,' said Mr Goddard to Captain Fielding, 'what did I tell you? She is an amazingly persistent woman.'

'Go and turn her out,' said Captain Fielding. 'Tell her it's highly improper for her to be sitting here in your house in the middle of the night.'

Mr Goddard sighed. The advice was well meant, but it was useless. He knew Miss Blow, and Captain Fielding did not.

'Mary,' he said, 'slip upstairs as quietly as you can, and get me my pyjamas and tooth brush. I'll have to go to the barrack for night. They'll give me some sort of a shake-down.'

'And will the young lady be sleeping here?' asked Mary.

'I expect so,' said Mr Goddard. 'If she does, she'll tell you so beforehand quite plainly. Make her as comfortable as you can.'

Mary went upstairs on tiptoe. Unfortunately, owing to

nervousness induced by excess of caution, she upset a hot-water can, which fell with a hideous clatter against Mr Goddard's bath. She hastened from the bedroom, and was met on the stairs by Miss Blow.

'What have you got there?' said Miss Blow, eyeing the pyjamas suspiciously.

'It's clothes from the wash,' said Mary. 'Now that the master's away, I thought I might as well be doing that as nothing.'

'You can tell him,' said Miss Blow, 'that I'm going to the hotel now, and that I'll be round to see him the first thing in the morning.'

She left the house, slamming the door behind her. Mary carried the pyjamas and the tooth brush upstairs again. Then she went into the kitchen and broke the happy news to her master and Captain Fielding.

'Thank God!' said Mr Goddard. 'I'm safe for tonight, anyway.'

'She'll be back with you in the morning,' said Captain Fielding, grinning. 'I don't see that you've much to congratulate yourself about.'

'Something may happen before then,' said Mr Goddard.

It is very seldom that things happen just when they are wanted to. The prisoner on the verge of execution hopes, but as a rule hopes in vain, for an earthquake at early dawn. The debtor whose bill is due the next day prays for, but scarcely expects, a fire in the bank premises during the night, an effective fire destructive of iron safes. Mr Goddard's feeling that something might happen before Miss Blow caught him again was hardly a hope. Nothing short of some wholly unprecedented event would be any use to him. But Mr Goddard was exceptionally fortunate. Something did happen. He was roused at six o'clock in the morning by a violent knocking at his door. He looked out of his window and saw Constable Moriarty standing in the street with a bicycle.

'What on earth do you want at this hour?' said Mr Goddard.

He had slept badly during the early part of the night, and was greatly annoyed at being roused from a doze at six o'clock.

'If it's Miss Blow you're after,' he went on, 'I haven't got her here. She's at the hotel. Go there and get her. Take her with you, if you want her. She's no use to me.'

Constable Moriarty grinned. He did not want Miss Blow any more than his officer did. Then, in the very middle of his grin, he grew grave again.

'It's what Sergeant Farrelly is after sending me over to tell you, sir, that the two English gentlemen that went off to Pool-a-donagh on their bicycles is after getting lost.'

'Lost! What do you mean by lost?'

'According to the word that came to the barrack at Clonmore, sir, the ladies arrived at Pool-a-donagh at four o'clock or thereabouts and didn't find the gentlemen. It was thought that maybe they'd taken a wrong turn, though it's hard to know how they could, seeing there isn't a wrong turn to take, and that they might have come back to Clonmore. So the sergeant at Pool-a-donagh sent a wire to Sergeant Farrelly; but he didn't know where they were, and no more did Jimmy O'Loughlin, for we asked him. We sent a few more wires to the barracks round about, but we got no tidings of them good nor bad. There was men out searching all night from Pool-a-donagh, and Constable Cole and the sergeant took a look round when they were on patrol. They do say the ladies was in a terrible state. There was a mounted man came into Clonmore between three and four this morning, and Sergeant Farrelly sent me over to you on a bicycle the way you'd be able to tell him what he'd better do.'

'I never heard of such a thing in my life,' said Mr Goddard. 'How can they be lost? The thing is impossible. Hang it all! They must be somewhere.'

'So you'd say, sir. But there isn't a police station anywhere round but it's been wired to, and not one has seen the gentle-men, dead or alive.'

'Don't talk about their being dead,' said Mr Goddard. 'Good heavens, man! They're Members of Parliament. If they've gone and committed suicide there'll be a most fright-ful row, and everybody will say it's the fault of the police. They must be found at once.'

Mr Goddard was in his pyjamas and dressing-gown. He told Constable Moriarty to go into the yard and harness the horse while he shaved and dressed. He was inclined at first to be angry with the Members of Parliament. It is a stupid thing to get lost, and men have no right to be stupid. He did not want to spend the day searching bohireens and bog-holes. He wanted to play in the Ballymoy tennis tournament. He had engaged himself as partner to Mrs Fielding, the Resident Magistrate's wife, and it vexed him to have to disappoint the lady. By degrees the matter began to present itself to him in a brighter light. He was now obliged, absolutely forced, to leave Ballymoy, and by leaving early he would escape Miss Blow, escape her for a time at all events. He reflected that if she sought him out with her usual relentlessness he would, in any case, have been unable to play in the tournament. A man can-not with any decency appear on a tennis court while a beauti-ful and angry girl hurls reproaches at him from the side lines. Even if he succeeded in evading her, his nerve would be shattered by the consciousness that she might appear beside him at any moment. It seemed to him that the loss of the Members of Parliament was, after all, a blessing in disguise; that, in fact, his wish had been fulfilled beyond his hope—something had happened.

He sat down and scribbled a note of apology for his absence.

'Dear Fielding,' he wrote, 'will you ask your wife to be so kind as to excuse me. I am exceedingly sorry to disappoint her, and I assure you I would not do it if I could possibly help it. Two Members of Parliament have disappeared during the night, and I have to go out and look for them. Perhaps the rector would play with Mrs Fielding if you asked him. He's no earthly good, but he's on the handicapping committee, and would let himself in soft. In any case she would get a game of some sort. If you happen to come across that good-looking girl in the grey dress, you might tell her that I promised to play today with Mrs Fielding, and that you expect me up at the club between twelve o'clock and four. That will keep her in Ballymoy for most of the day, anyhow. The Lord knows I don't want her on my track. I shall have worry enough without that.'

He stuffed some biscuits into his pocket and went out into the yard. Constable Moriarty promised to deliver the note to Captain Fielding. Mr Goddard got into his trap and drove off. He had to pass the hotel on his way, and was half afraid that Miss Blow might sally out and seize the horse's head. She did not. It was not yet seven o'clock, and the blinds of all the upstairs rooms were drawn down. Miss Blow was, apparently, sleeping off the fatigue of the day before.

Mr Goddard reached Clonmore at half-past eight. He found Sergeant Farrelly and Constable Cole at breakfast. They had been up all night, and were looking fagged, nervous, and harassed.

'There's two more wires, sir, that's come in since eight this morning. The one of them says that there's no further news of the missing gentlemen in Pool-a-donagh, and the other says that the ladies started back to Clonmore at seven this morning, and is in hopes that you'll be here to meet them when they arrive.'

'If I'm not,' said Mr Goddard—'and it's quite possible that I won't—if I'm not, you'll have to see them, sergeant. They're very nice ladies,' he added, noticing a gloom on Sergeant Farrelly's face, 'not the least like Miss Blow.'

'It's a queer thing,' said Sergeant Farrelly, 'that a man could get lost between this and Pool-a-donagh. It's a straight road, and they got started right on it. Jimmy O'Loughlin was telling me last night that he seen them going through the town, and them heading straight on the same as if they knew the place all their lives. Without they took a boat and went out to sea in it—and I don't know where they'd get a boat along that road—it's a queer thing.'

'It is a queer thing,' said Mr Goddard. 'But what's the use of spending the morning saying so? Show me all the telegrams that came last night.'

He worked his way through a sheaf of pink forms. The messages were, for the most part, very monotonous. In language which hardly varied and with a strict attention to the number of words which can be sent for sixpence, the sergeants of all the police barracks within a wide circle disclaimed any knowledge of the missing gentlemen. No one had seen them. The most careful inquiries brought no information. Here and there, among these cold, official statements, Mr Goddard came upon a message which breathed anxiety, heartbreak, and despair, a despatch from a wife or an aunt. These were verbose, reckless of expense, and always ended by urging the necessity of immediate action on the part of the police.

'I can't do anything,' said Mr Goddard; 'at all events, I won't do anything till I've had some breakfast. It's after nine now. I'll go down to the hotel and see what I can get out of Jimmy O'Loughlin.'

He found, when he reached the hotel, that the table in the commercial room was laid for breakfast. A pleasant scent of frying bacon reached him from the kitchen. He became aware that he was extremely hungry.

'Jimmy!' he called. 'Jimmy O'Loughlin!'

'Is that yourself, Mr Goddard?' said Jimmy, speaking from the top of the stairs. 'They're just getting the breakfast ready for the doctor's young lady. I'll tell them to fry a couple more eggs for you. She'll be glad of your company. It's lonely for the creature taking her meals by herself, and her in trouble about the loss of the doctor and all.'

Jimmy O'Loughlin in his shirt-sleeves and without a collar

leaned over the banisters as he spoke. The grin on his face was malicious.

'Is Miss Blow here?' said Mr Goddard. 'I don't believe she is. How could she?'

'She is not here,' said Jimmy, 'but I'm just after getting a wire from her to say that she'll be in for her breakfast at half-past nine. It must be that now, if it isn't past it. Bridgy! Are you there, Bridgy? I say, will you fry a couple of eggs and some rashers for Mr Goddard? He'll be taking his breakfast along with the doctor's young lady as soon as she comes.'

'Look here,' said Mr Goddard, 'there's no use your trying to pull my leg this way. Miss Blow can't be here. She was sound asleep when I left Ballymoy at seven, and she couldn't possibly do the drive in the time.'

'Not if she drove,' said Jimmy; 'but she'd do it on a bicycle.'

'How do you know she has a bicycle?'

'I don't know. How would I? All I say is that, being the sort of young lady she is, it's likely she'd get a bicycle, or for the matter of that a motor car, if so she wanted one. Anyway, she'll be here at half-past nine, for that's what she said.'

'Then,' said Mr Goddard 'I'll not stay for breakfast. I'm going up to the Castle. I have business with Lord Manton. And look here, Jimmy, when Miss Blow arrives, if she does arrive, there'll be no need for you to say anything about my being here. It would only upset her.'

'I will not. Why would I? Hasn't she trouble enough without that? But tell me now, Mr Goddard, is it true what I hear them saying about them gentlemen that was through the town yesterday on their bicycles?'

'Is what true?'

'That they're off.'

'They're lost,' said Mr Goddard, 'if that's what you mean.'

Jimmy O'Loughlin winked. 'The same as the poor doctor,' he said, 'and Patsy Devlin.'

'Not in the least the same. We know what happened to them well enough. But these fellows are quite different. But I can't stop here talking to you all morning. I've got something else to do. Don't say anything to anybody about my being up at the Castle.'

'I will not. If I open my mouth about you at all, I'll say you're searching high and low for the men that's gone.'

16

'HIS lordship is still at breakfast, sir,' said Wilkins.

'Will you ask him if I can speak to him for a few minutes as soon as he has finished?' said Mr Goddard.

He was shown into the library, where Lord Manton's letters and newspapers were arranged on a table near the window. He was an old gentleman who declined to do business of any kind, even open a letter, before breakfast. He attributed his good health to his habit of facing the kind of worries which the post brings only when he was fortified by a solid meal. Mr Goddard glanced at the columns of a Dublin evening paper of the day before, half fearful of a scare headline announcing the loss of two Members of Parliament in Connemara. He was delighted to find that the editor had been able to discover nothing more exciting than a crisis in the Balkans and a speech by the Prime Minister. Wilkins entered the room.

'His lordship's compliments,' he said, 'and he will be pleased if you will join him at breakfast.'

Mr Goddard accepted the invitation gladly. The smell of Jimmy O'Loughlin's bacon and eggs had whetted his appetite. He was conducted to the dining-room by Wilkins, and found

Lord Manton seated by himself at the end of a large table. The dining-room in Clonmore Castle is a spacious and well-proportioned apartment. A tradition exists that in the time of Lord Manton's father, on the occasion of a county election, fifty gentlemen once sat down in it together at dinner. In those days, no doubt, people did not object to being crowded. But even today thirty people could very comfortably have dined in the room, and there would still have been space for the servants to make their way about. It was the largest room in the Castle, and its present proprietor looked singularly small, even insignificant, seated alone in the middle of it. Lord Manton greeted his guest cheerfully.

'Good morning, Mr Goddard. This is an early visit. Have you by any chance come across the body of Dr O'Grady? Won't you help yourself to something to eat? You'll find whatever there is on the side table.'

Mr Goddard secured a kidney and some bacon.

'No,' he said; 'there's no news of Dr O'Grady.'

'Have you got engaged to be married to Miss Blow?' said Lord Manton. 'That's the way this business will end, I expect. That young woman came over here for a husband, and now that the doctor has bolted there is only you or me for her to choose. So far as I can see at present, she seems to prefer you. I'm very glad she does. In fact, I'm keeping out of her way as much as I can.'

'So am I; but it's rather difficult.'

'I suppose it is. I hear that she went the whole way over to Ballymoy after you last night; walked every step of it. I'm surprised that you escaped her after that. How did you manage it? I should have thought you could hardly have refused to marry her without being actually rude. But perhaps that story is only gossip.'

'It's quite true,' said Mr Goddard. 'But Lord Manton, I came up here this morning to speak to you about—the fact is, I am in a serious difficulty.'

'You are. I can scarcely imagine anything more serious.'

'I wanted,' said Mr Goddard, 'to ask your advice about——'

'You shall have it. Give in and marry her at once with a good grace. That's my advice. After all, you might do a great deal worse. She's a very good looking girl, and by her own account she'll have some money. It's far better for you to pretend you like it. It's no earthly use your trying to escape if her mind is made up. Your plan of dodging up and down between Clonmore and Ballymoy can't be kept up for ever. Sooner or later she'll overtake you in one place or the other; or else she'll meet you on the road between the two, where you'll be quite at her mercy.'

'I dare say you're right,' said Mr Goddard. 'But it's not about Miss Blow that I want to consult you this morning. Did you hear about the Members of Parliament?'

'I heard that two Members of Parliament went through the town on bicycles yesterday,' said Lord Manton, 'with a lot of woman after them on cars; Suffragettes, I suppose, pursuing them for votes. It's astonishing how they track those poor fellows to the remotest ends of the earth. '

'They've disappeared,' said Mr Goddard.

'Sensible men. That was by far the wisest thing they could do. But I wonder how they managed it? You haven't been able to disappear from Miss Blow. We must find out about it. I may have to disappear myself when that question comes up to the House of Lords.'

'You've not got it right,' said Mr Goddard. 'The women on the cars were their wives. Or rather two of them were. The other was their aunt.'

'Dear me! Is that legal? That sort of group marriage with a common aunt doesn't seem to me quite the thing for Members of Parliament.'

'They had one wife each, of course,' said Mr Goddard, 'and the aunt only belonged to one of them. They have the police roused all over the country looking for them. That's what brings me here this morning. I've got to do something to find them.'

'Do you mean to tell me that these two men have got lost in such a way that they can't be found?'

'They have. It's really a most extraordinary thing. They started on bicycles yesterday from Clonmore to ride to Pool-a-donagh. They never arrived. That's really all we know about the matter. The ladies followed them on a car and didn't overtake them. We've telegraphed to every police barrack in the neighbourhood, and they haven't turned up anywhere.'

'I'll tell you what it is, Goddard. This is an uncommonly awkward business for you. Here you are, responsible for the safety of the inhabitants of this district, and no less than four men disappear completely in the inside of a single week. First there was Dr O'Grady. Then poor Patsy Devlin vanished, leaving a wife and family behind him.'

'We know all about them,' said Mr Goddard.

'And now no less than two Members of Parliament. It doesn't look at all well. I'm greatly afraid there'll be a fuss when it gets into the newspapers. The public will take the keenest interest in it. We shall have columns and columns every day. Do you happen to know whether these men were Liberals or Conservatives?'

'No, I don't. I don't see that it makes any difference. I've got to find them whichever they are.'

'It makes the greatest difference,' said Lord Manton. 'If they're supporters of the Government, there'll be a much bigger fuss than if they're on the Opposition side. The Prime Minister isn't likely to sit down quietly under the loss of two votes, especially with the way by-elections are going at present. You'll simply have to find them.'

'I wish I could,' said Mr Goddard. 'I'd do it quick enough, whatever their politics are, if I knew how to go about it.'

'Of course, if they belonged to the Opposition,' said Lord Manton, 'the matter won't be pressed by the Government. But even so you'll have the newspapers to reckon with, and the curiosity of the general public. Why don't you go and look for them?'

'I would go at once, if I had the remotest idea where to look. But I haven't. That's what I want your advice about.'

'You say,' said Lord Manton, 'that there are three ladies belonging to them. If I were you, I should begin by introducing them to Miss Blow. Then get a hold of Mrs Patsy Devlin and let her talk to the whole party. You could put them all together into a room at Jimmy O'Loughlin's hotel. They'll interest each other. They have so much in common.'

'I might do that, of course. But I don't see what good it would be. I shouldn't be any nearer finding the men.'

'No, you wouldn't; but you'd have time to turn round and think things out a bit. They'd be sure to talk for a good while once you got them started, and it's quite possible that by the time they'd finished, the two men might have turned up somewhere or other.'

'I don't see what can possibly have happened to them,' said Mr Goddard. 'After you pass Rosivera the road runs the whole way between the bog and the sea. They couldn't get off it if they tried. And they must have got as far as Rosivera when they started right, for there isn't a cross road between this and there. Even if they were fools enough to go up some bohireen or other, they'd only have to turn round and come down again.'

'That seems to me,' said Lord Manton, 'to knock the bottom out of the theory that they've got lost. As you say, they can't be lost. They might sit down on the side of the road and cry; but if they did the women on the cars would have seen them.'

'I've thought all that out. I can't see how they've got lost; but the fact is they are lost.'

'I don't believe it,' said Lord Manton.

'Surely you don't suppose that they're playing off a practical joke on us.'

'Come in the library and have a smoke,' said Lord Manton.

'I'm not so sure that I ought to. With this business on my hands I scarcely feel justified—I think I should——'

'Oh, nonsense. You can't do anything until you've thought.

Premature and imperfectly considered action in a case like this is always a mistake, and you can't possibly think properly without tobacco.'

Lord Manton kept excellent cigars for his guests. Mr Goddard, who had smoked them before, lit one with pleasure, and stretched himself in a deep chair. He had breakfasted heartily, in spite of anxiety and worry. He felt that a short rest was due to him. He was prepared to believe that a period of calm reflection was due to the case of the two errant Members of Parliament. Lord Manton did not smoke his own cigars, and rarely lay back in his own very comfortable chairs. He preferred an upright kind of seat, and he smoked cigarettes, lighting them one after another in rapid succession, while he talked, wrote or thought. On this occasion he did not remain seated for more than a couple of minutes. Before his first cigarette was half smoked he stood up and talked down to Mr Goddard from a commanding position beside the chimney-piece.

'I don't believe,' he said, 'I don't for one moment believe, that those Members of Parliament are lost.'

'Lost or disappeared or stolen,' said Mr Goddard, 'it's all the same so far as I am concerned. I've got to find them.'

'It's not in the least the same thing. If they were simply lost in the way a child or a dog or a collar stud gets lost, then you'd know where to look for them. Draw a circle of, say, ten miles in diameter, with Rosivera for its centre, and they must be inside of it somewhere. You've only got to put men enough on the job and you're bound to find them. But if they have disappeared of their own accord, vanished intentionally and deliberately, then you will have to proceed in quite a different way.'

'It's all very well to talk of Dr O'Grady and Patsy Devlin disappearing like that; but it's different with these men. Why the devil should they disappear?'

'They can't have got lost,' said Lord Manton. 'You satisfied me, if you did not satisfy yourself, about that; and if they're not lost they must have bolted. How else can you account for their not turning up?'

'But why should they? What had they to run away from?'

'That, of course, I can't say for certain, for I don't know the men. But, taking into consideration the little I do know about them, I can make a guess. Can't you imagine it? They had with them three women, two wives and an aunt. The one who hadn't his aunt with him very probably has one at home, and it's quite possible that they both have sisters.'

'I dare say they have, I didn't ask.'

'Well now, think. They were English Members of Parliament, and therefore presumably pretty well to do. They probably had businesses somewhere, and residences in a suburban district. What does all that mean? Respectability. Imagine to yourself the appalling weight of respectability involved in the possession of a wife, an aunt, a sister, a business, investments, and a seat in Parliament. Can't you fancy the poor fellows coming to find it all perfectly intolerable; saying to each other: "Hang it, let's get off and run loose for a while"? I don't say I'm right. I can't be sure, because I don't know the men, and I didn't see the women; but what I'm offering you is an intelligible explanation of the facts. I can't see any other explanation. What sort of women were they? What were they like?'

'I don't know. I didn't notice anything particular about them. They were just ordinary women.'

'There you are,' said Lord Manton. 'It's your ordinary, well-behaved woman who drives a man perfectly frantic if he has any spirit in him. I couldn't live with an ordinary woman for three months at a stretch. Look at my daughter, for instance. How long do you suppose I could stand her? Certainly not three months, not two months, I'm at the end of my tether after a six weeks' visit to her. And I'm not married to her. I haven't got to be very close to her. I haven't got to see her in a red dressing-gown combing her hair. I haven't got to listen to the noise she makes when she's washing her teeth.

You don't understand these things because you're not married. Very likely you never will understand them, because Miss Blow's not an ordinary woman——'

'She is not,' said Mr Goddard.

But these two poor fellows,' said Lord Manton, 'had got to do with ordinary women. They had to give their opinions on new hats, had to listen to stories about the things which the servants did or didn't do. Of course they bolted.'

'I wish to goodness they'd have bolted out of some other district, then, if they had to bolt. Why should they come here? You'd think it would be much more convenient to run away from a place like London than from Clonmore. But I don't believe they have bolted.'

'They can't have got lost. The thing's absurd on the face of it. Take a single point in addition to all those that you've made already. Take their bicycles. A man might accidentally lose himself, but his bicycle couldn't possibly get lost. He must leave it on the side of the road somewhere, and wherever he leaves it you're sure to find it. You can get rid of a bicycle on purpose, though even that's not so easy. Sinking it in the sea is about the only way I can imagine of effectually disposing of it. But you can't lose it and yourself. Nobody could lose both himself and a bicycle unless he did it on purpose.'

'But——' said Mr Goddard.

He had a whole series of criticisms utterly destructive of Lord Manton's hypothesis. He had seen the Members of Parliament. He felt that he knew them. He found it impossible to imagine their breaking out into wild Bohemianism, sickening of respectability, rebelling against the monotony of any woman, however ordinary. There was Mr Dick, who had bounded out of the railway carriage, volatile, debonair, gay with familiar quotations. There was Mr Sanders, rigid, mathematical, a little morose on account of his weak heart. Lord Manton might conceivably find an ordinary woman maddening; but Mr Dick, once he began, would go on kissing her contentedly for years and years. He would appreciate the way in

167

which his dinner was cooked for him. Mr Sanders would appreciate that too. He might be a little exacting, would, no doubt, expect his weak heart to be taken seriously, would put a woman in her proper place in the settled order of things, and keep her there. But both Mr Dick and Mr Sanders would recognize that a woman must be allowed to wash her teeth. They would not resent the noise of the water gurgling in her mouth. They would both know that women must comb their hair, and that a red dressing-gown is a suitable and convenient garment under certain circumstances. They would not be angry when they were told about the misdeeds of maid-servants, a trying and exhausting class to deal with. They were men with well-balanced minds, men of practical common sense, men who would not fly blindly in the face of facts. They were not the men to run away from their wives, or even from their aunts.

'But——' he began again.

Lord Manton lit a fresh cigarette, his fourth, and waited. Mr Goddard sought for words in which to express his feelings. He might have found them in time, but time was not given him. Wilkins entered the room.

'There is a lady to see you, sir,' he said to Mr Goddard. 'I showed her into the small drawing-room. She said she wished to see you particular.'

'Good God!' said Mr Goddard, 'It's Miss Blow!'

'Is it Miss Blow?' said Lord Manton to Wilkins. 'Don't attempt to break the news to him if it is. Tell him straight out. It's kinder in the end.'

'It's the same young lady,' said Wilkins, 'that called on your lordship two days ago.'

'The young lady that was talking about bringing a corpse here? I told you, I remember, to get white flowers from the gardener. Is it that young lady?'

'Yes, my lord.'

'And has she brought it this time?'

'Not that I saw, my lord.'

'If you didn't see it, Wilkins, I think we may take it for granted that it isn't there.'

'Damn that girl!' said Mr Goddard. 'You'd think I had enough on my hands without her.'

'From the way you're speaking of her,' said Lord Manton, 'I suppose you don't feel inclined to go into the drawing-room and offer to marry her. That, as I said before, is the proper thing for you to do. If you won't the only other course I see open to you is to get away out of this as fast as you can.'

'What's the good? She'd be after me again at once.'

'Not at once,' said Lord Manton. 'I think I can arrange to give you a good long start. Wilkins will go back and ask her to be good enough to remain where she is for a few minutes. You could tell her, Wilkins, that Mr Goddard is engaged with me at present, discussing very important business, but that he'll be with her in less than a quarter of an hour. You could do that, Wilkins, couldn't you?'

'Yes, my lord.'

'Then Mr Goddard could get out of the house and walk across the deer park. You could run if you like, Goddard, keeping carefully out of sight of the drawing-room windows. After a time, say at the end of half an hour, Miss Blow will begin to get impatient. What do you suppose she'll do when she gets impatient, Wilkins?'

'I'd say, my lord, that's she's likely to ring the bell.'

'Exactly. That's what I thought myself. I suppose, Wilkins, that you could arrange for the under housemaid to go to her when she rings.'

'Yes, my lord.'

'And the under housemaid would, of course, know nothing about Mr Goddard. What would the under housemaid do, Wilkins, when she was asked about Mr Goddard, and knew nothing about him?'

'I'd say, my lord, that she'd tell the young lady she'd go to make inquiries.'

'Quite so. She'd be sure to do that. But she needn't go back again to Miss Blow. She could resume her interrupted duties. She could start off under-housemaiding again at the place she left off when Miss Blow rang the bell. I presume that, after a decent interval, say a quarter of an hour, Miss Blow would ring the bell again; this time the upper housemaid could go to her. That could be arranged, I suppose, Wilkins?'

'Certainly, my lord.'

'She, of course, would know nothing about Mr Goddard; but she would promise to go and make inquiries. She would then get back to her upper-housemaiding and completely forget about Miss Blow. After another interval, this time probably a shorter one, say ten minutes, Miss Blow would ring the bell again. Then the cook could go to her, and, of course——'

'Beg pardon, my lord, but the cook wouldn't go.'

'Couldn't you arrange it, Wilkins?'

'No, my lord; it's not the cook's place to answer bells.'

'I forgot that,' said Lord Manton. 'It was stupid of me. I should have remembered. I'm afraid, Wilkins, that you'd have to go yourself the third time. You would tell her that Mr Goddard had left the house an hour before. It would be about an hour, wouldn't it, Wilkins?'

'As near as I can go to it, it would be about that, my lord.'

'After that I should recommend you to leave the room at once, Wilkins. You can stay if you like and see what happens, but I rather recommend you to leave at once.'

'Yes, my lord.'

'Very well. That gives you a clear hour's start, Goddard. You'd better be off at once.'

'Where am I to go to?'

'I really don't know. I'm not advising you to run away. I think it would be wiser for you to stay here and marry Miss Blow without any further resistance. If you act contrary to my advice, you mustn't expect me to make your plans for you.'

Mr Goddard and Wilkins left the room together. Lord Manton lit a fresh cigarette and tried to make up his mind whether he would like to see Miss Blow before she left the house. He felt sure that the interview, if he ventured on it, would be an interesting one, and that Miss Blow would say very amusing things. On the other hand, he had a vivid recollection of the masterful way in which she compelled him to write a note to Sergeant Farrelly. It seemed likely that she would attempt something of the same sort again. He was most unwilling to get further entangled in the mystery of Dr O'Grady's disappearance. He was still turning the question over in his mind when Mr Goddard burst noisily into the room.

17

'Hullo!' said Lord Manton. 'Back again. What have you forgotten? It's rather rash of you to venture, I think. If it's only your cigar-case or something of that sort that you've left behind, I should have had it posted after you as soon as you sent me your address. I can't keep Miss Blow here permanently, you know. In dealing with a lady like her you ought not to take these risks.'

'The others are coming,' said Mr Goddard breathlessly.

'Oh, indeed! What others?'

'I met them in the deer park. They are coming up here. They had Jimmy O'Loughlin's boy with them to show them the way.'

'What others?'

'I turned at once and ran back,' said Mr Goddard. 'I don't think they saw me; in fact, I'm sure they didn't. But what are we to do now?'

'I'd stand a better chance of answering that question,' said Lord Manton, 'if I knew who you were talking about.'

'The other women, Mrs Dick and——'

'Oh, the wives of the lost Members of Parliament.'

'Yes. What shall we do?'

'Don't say, what shall *we* do,' said Lord Manton. 'I'm not going to do anything except sit here and watch the progress of events. I think that's as much as can be expected of me. Many men wouldn't do even that. I know lots of people who'd object to your way of filling up their houses with strange women; but I'm giving you every latitude. If you choose to interview your lady friends in my drawing-room, I make no objection. But I won't be dragged into any complications myself. That's the reason I don't like your saying "we". The question is not what shall we do, but what will you do.'

'What shall I do then?' said Mr Goddard.

'If you'd taken my advice,' said Lord Manton, 'and married Miss Blow half an hour ago, you wouldn't be in this difficulty now. Your course would have been perfectly plain. You'd simply have referred the other ladies to Miss Blow. She would have dealt with them, and not allowed them to do you any harm. However, I don't want to rub in your past mistakes. The only course open to you now is to introduce these three to Miss Blow and let them talk the matter over quietly together while you get Mrs Patsy Devlin to join them.'

Wilkins entered the room while Lord Manton was speaking.

'There are some ladies to see your lordship,' he said.

'To see me? To see Mr Goddard, you mean.'

'It was your lordship they asked for.'

'There must be some mistake,' said Lord Manton. 'Go to them again, Wilkins, and say that Mr Goddard is here and will be delighted to see them.'

'I don't see what good that will be,' said Mr Goddard. 'Wait a minute.'

But Wilkins was gone. Mr Goddard made a protest.

'Why did you give me away like that?' he asked. 'If you

hadn't told them I was here, they would never have thought of asking for me.'

'I gave you away to save myself,' said Lord Manton. 'I always give other people away when there's any kind of unpleasantness going on. That has been a fixed rule of mine through life, and I've always found it works well.'

'Beg pardon, my lord,' said Wilkins, who returned, 'but the ladies say it's your lordship they want to see; but they'll be very glad to meet Mr Goddard too.'

'Did you ask their business, Wilkins?'

'I did, my lord. They said they heard that you were a magistrate, and——'

'That,' said Lord Manton, 'sounds about as bad as anything could be. How many ladies were there, Wilkins?'

'Three, my lord.'

'The whole three,' said Mr Goddard. 'I told you so.'

'Where have you put them, Wilkins?'

'I showed them into the big drawing-room, my lord. The other lady was in——'

'Well, go and change them out of that into the small drawing-room. Or, wait a minute. It may be easier to move Miss Blow. Go and put her into the big drawing-room along with the other three. Then shut the door and leave them. Do you think you can manage that, Wilkins?'

'I could try, my lord.'

'Very well. Go and try. And if you succeed, don't go to them again until they've rung the bell at least a dozen times.'

'Certainly not, my lord.'

'It's rather hard on a man of my age,' said Lord Manton, 'to be hunted out of my own house in this way by a lot of strange women. I'm not blaming you, Goddard. All the same, if you had been reasonable about Miss Blow we wouldn't be in the position we are. Now, of course, there's nothing for it but to fly. It's very undignified for me, being a peer and that sort of thing. It will also, I'm afraid, be most uncomfortable. I mind that much more than the humiliation. But there's nothing else for it. If I stay here they'll catch me sooner or later.'

'What will you do?'

'I shall get out a horse and trap if I can without being noticed. I shall drive down to the station, and lie hid in the ticket office until the next train is due. Then I shall go to London. You'd better come with me.'

Lord Manton's idea was to reach the stableyard by way of the servants' quarters, so as to avoid passing the doors of either the big or the small drawing-room. To do this from the library it was necessary to go along a corridor and then cross an angle of the central hall off which both the drawing-rooms opened. The corridor was safe. The passage across the hall was dangerous. Unless Wilkins actually locked the ladies in, a door might be opened at any moment.

Lord Manton and Mr Goddard went on tiptoe along the corridor. A voice reached them from the hall. It was Wilkins' voice.

'This way, miss, if you please.'

'One of them has escaped,' said Mr Goddard.

'No,' whispered Lord Manton; 'it's only Wilkins moving Miss Blow into the big drawing-room. Wait a minute.'

They heard Wilkins' voice again. This time it was nearer than it had been.

'I beg your pardon, miss, but if you'll allow me to show you the way. You're going in quite the wrong direction, miss.'

Mr Goddard clutched Lord Manton's arm. 'She's coming down here,' he said. 'We'd better——'

'It's all right,' whispered Lord Manton. 'Wilkins will head her off.'

'I'm going in the direction in which I mean to go.'

This voice was unmistakably Miss Blow's. It was clear, resonant, determined, and sounded very near at hand.

'Good heavens!' said Mr Goddard.

'She's quite right,' said Lord Manton. 'She is going in the direction in which she means to go. I rather respect her for it.'

Wilkins, walking sideways, and expostulating vehemently, appeared at the end of the corridor. Behind him, mistress of herself and the situation, strode Miss Blow. She caught sight of Lord Manton and Mr Goddard at once. She pointed to them with a finger and fixed her eyes upon them with a terrible glare. They stood still, fascinated. The idea of escape by running and a leap through the library window occurred to Lord Manton. But with Miss Blow's eyes on him he was incapable of the effort. Wilkins, faithful to the last, walked backwards along the corridor, in front of Miss Blow. He looked as if he meant to sacrifice himself in order to stand between his master and Amazonian violence. He was a good servant.

'So there you are,' said Miss Blow. 'You——' Her finger, pointed at Mr Goddard, trembled with indignant scorn. 'And you, my lord.'

There was a fine note of contempt, bitter and furious contempt, in her voice, as she uttered the words 'my lord'. There was something terrible in the association of a title reckoned honourable by the world with the baseness which she evidently attributed to Lord Manton.

'Yes,' said Lord Manton; 'we're both here. But why aren't you in the big drawing-room with the other ladies? You oughtn't to come down here, you know, especially without a chaperone.'

'You call yourselves gentlemen,' said Miss Blow.

'No,' said Lord Manton; 'we don't. I certainly don't. And I should be surprised to hear that Mr Goddard did. The word is quite out of fashion, I assure you. Nobody uses it nowadays. Don't bring unjust charges against us, Miss Blow. There are lots of things we may be accused of with truth. We're not the men we ought to be, especially Mr Goddard. Charge us with the things we've done, and we'll confess at once and apologize. But don't be unjust. We never called ourselves gentlemen.'

'You ran away from me yesterday,' said Miss Blow, addressing Mr Goddard, 'after promising faithfully that you'd help me. You ran away again today. You would be running away now if I hadn't caught you in the act.'

'He did and he would,' said Lord Manton. 'I've just been speaking to him about it. I told him his conduct was disgraceful. I'm glad now that he'll hear what you think of it from your own lips. It'll do him good.'

Mr Goddard frowned and shuffled uneasily. Even though he had been fairly warned of the principle on which Lord Manton treated his friends in emergencies, he did not expect to be sacrificed so completely and remorselessly.

'You're as bad yourself,' said Miss Blow.

'No,' said Lord Manton; 'I'm not. Try to be just, Miss Blow. I didn't run away from you.'

'You're just as bad as he is,' said Miss Blow.

Her voice was clear and loud. Lord Manton glanced anxiously towards the hall. It was quite possible that the noise of the denunciation might reach the big drawing-room.

'Wilkins,' he said, 'did you shut the door of the big drawing-room?'

'No, my lord; I understood your lordship to say that this lady——'

'Then go and do it at once. I can't have the other three—— Miss Blow is speaking to us in a confidential manner and doesn't want——'

'Who are you shutting up?' said Miss Blow. 'Who is your lackey going to imprison?'

'Some ladies,' said Lord Manton. 'There are, I believe, three of them. But I'm not imprisoning them. I'm only trying to keep them where they are for a few minutes. I'm doing it entirely on your account. They wouldn't be at all cheering company for you. They have, unfortunately, just lost their husbands under the most mysterious and trying circumstances. Members of Parliament, you know. Excellent fellows every one of them. The whole thing is unspeakably sad.'

'Are those the ladies——?' said Miss Blow. 'But of course they are. I heard about that. Do you mean to say that you're going to sit here and do nothing, nothing whatever, while men are being murdered in this wholesale manner every day? Will you make no effort to bring the criminals to justice and prevent the loss of more human life? You, sir,' she addressed Mr Goddard, 'you wear his Majesty's uniform; you are an officer in what is supposed to be a police force——'

'It is a police force,' said Mr Goddard feebly. 'It really is, although I am an officer in it.'

'And you,' she went on, turning to Lord Manton, 'you are a magistrate besides being a peer.'

'Miss Blow,' said Lord Manton, 'won't you come into the library and sit down? We could talk so much more comfortably if we were sitting down. Besides, this is rather a public place for the discussion of private affairs.'

He looked past Miss Blow towards the end of the corridor. Something in his expression made Miss Blow turn her head. She saw, gathered in a knot in the hall, the cook, the kitchenmaid, the upper and under housemaid, and Wilkins. All of them, except Wilkins, were grinning. They had forgotten all decency and the respect due to their master. They were eagerly listening to every word Miss Blow said. She allowed herself to be led into the library.

'Now sit down,' said Lord Manton. 'You must be thoroughly tired out after your long walk yesterday and all this excitement today. Will you allow me to offer you a glass of wine and a biscuit? Goddard, ring the bell, like a good man.'

'No,' said Miss Blow.

'A cup of tea, then? No? Or an egg flip? The cook would have it ready in a moment. I often have an egg flip myself when I'm feeling over-done. It's an excellent thing, I assure you.'

'No,' said Miss Blow; 'I'll take nothing—nothing from you. I——'

'Well, just allow me to say one word,' said Lord Manton, 'before you begin again.'

'If you've any excuse to make for your behaviour,' said Miss Blow, 'make it. I shall listen to you.'

'I haven't,' said Lord Manton. 'Not a shred. Nor has Mr Goddard. Don't interrupt me, Goddard. You haven't any real excuse, and you know it. But you mustn't be too hard upon us, Miss Blow. Try to put yourself in our position, in Mr Goddard's position, for I really haven't anything to do with the business one way or other. It wasn't his fault about those Members of Parliament. He's just as sorry about it as anybody else. If he'd known that they intended to run away from their wives he'd have stopped them; but how could he know?'

'Oh!' said Miss Blow. 'That is the latest theory, is it? Their husbands ran away from them? Do you expect to get any one to believe that? I suppose the husband of that poor woman down in the village ran away from her. I suppose you mean to try and prove that she ill-treated him, that she, a half-starved, delicate woman, bullied a great hulking blacksmith. I suppose you'll say that Dr O'Grady ran away from me. Last time I was here you said he ran away from his creditors. When I proved that to be a lie, you have the assurance to say that he ran away from me.'

'I hadn't mentioned you or Dr O'Grady,' said Lord Manton. 'But come now, Miss Blow, be reasonable. If he has run away from you, he wouldn't be the only man that has. You can't deny that Mr Goddard ran away from you. He did it twice. You said so yourself. In fact, you more than hinted that he was in the act of a third flight when you caught him. There's nothing inherently absurd in supposing that one man would do what another man has done several times. I needn't say I wouldn't do it myself. But that's another matter. It's far better for you to look facts straight in the face, however unpleasant they are.'

Whether Miss Blow looked at the facts or not, the facts as Lord Manton represented them, she certainly looked at Mr Goddard. It seemed for a moment as if she was about to re-open the question of his flight to Ballymoy and his subsequent

178

flight back again to Clonmore. He felt greatly annoyed with Lord Manton for calling fresh attention to these performances. There ought, he was convinced, to be some limit to the extent to which a man may give away his friends. But Miss Blow recognized that these hurried flittings of his and the causes of them were side issues. She got back, with an evident effort, to the main point immediately under discussion.

'And why should you suppose that the husbands of the ladies you have shut up in your drawing-room have run away from them?'

It was of Lord Manton that she asked the question; but Mr Goddard answered her. He saw his opportunity and seized it. Having been sacrificed more than once as a burnt-offering to Miss Blow's wrath, he was perfectly ready, now that he got the chance, to show up Lord Manton, as a man who also deserved strong denunciation.

'Lord Manton says,' said Mr Goddard, 'that their husbands couldn't bear to live with them any more, because they were ordinary women and——'

'As well as I recollect,' said Lord Manton, 'it was you who used the word "ordinary". I hadn't seen the ladies at the time. For that matter, I haven't seen them yet.'

'And,' said Mr Goddard, speaking slowly and with emphasis, 'because they wear red dressing-gowns and wash their teeth.'

He glanced at Lord Manton with an expression of triumph on his face. Miss Blow stared first at one of the men before her and then at the other. She was amazed. In spite of the white heat of her virtuous indignation she was reduced for the moment to silence, a silence of sheer astonishment. The nature of the charge brought against the wives of the Members of Parliament took her aback. It was totally unexpected.

'Those,' said Mr Goddard, striking home after his victory, 'are the exact expressions Lord Manton used.'

'Of course,' said Lord Manton, in an explanatory and half-apologetic tone, 'I didn't mean to suggest that those were

Patsy Devlin's reasons for absconding. I don't suppose that his wife has a dressing-gown of any colour, and as for her teeth——'

Miss Blow began to recover a little from her first shock.

'Do you mean to say,' she said, 'that you consider a man is justified in deserting his wife because she wears a red dressing-gown and washes her teeth?'

'Certainly,' said Lord Manton. 'If you consider the matter fairly and impartially, without bias in favour of either sex, you will see that there can't be two opinions about it. The mere act of wearing a dressing-gown, red or blue, is of course nothing in itself. But considered as an expression of a certain spirit, of what I may perhaps call the spirit of persistent, puritanical domesticity; regarded as an evidence of an oppressive kind of civilized respectability, taken in conjunction with a whole series of trifling, or apparently trifling, mental and physical habits,—ordering dinner, for instance, engaging servants, doing needlework, paying weekly bills, keeping a visiting list, taking a holiday every year at the seaside—you will, I am sure, understand the sort of things I mean—taken in conjunction with these and regarded as an expression of the kind of spirit which takes a delight in doing these things and doing them continuously year after year—considered in this way, the wearing of a red dressing-gown does justify a man, a certain sort of man, in deserting his wife. You catch my meaning, I am sure, Miss Blow.'

Once more Miss Blow was silent from sheer astonishment. Then, after a pause, she spoke, and Mr Goddard, like the governor Felix before the Apostle Paul, trembled. Lord Manton, although it was to him that her remark was specially addressed, bore himself more bravely.

'You think it very fine,' she said, 'to bully and badger a helpless girl, and to allow innocent men to be murdered under your very eyes. But you'll have to answer for it. You'll be held responsible, both of you. It's—it's intolerable.'

'My dear Miss Blow,' said Lord Manton.

'Don't dare to say "my dear" to me.'

'I didn't mean it,' said Lord Manton, quite truthfully. 'Nothing was further from my mind than any idea of expressing affection, although of course I have a great regard and esteem for you. But do try to be reasonable. We're quite ready, both of us—I'm sure I may speak for Mr Goddard as well as myself—to do anything in our power. But what can we do? What do you suggest our doing? What do you want us to do?'

'Arrest the murderers,' said Miss Blow.

'Certainly,' said Lord Manton, 'Goddard, go at once and arrest the murderers. You're a policeman. It's your business to arrest murderers. Don't waste time. Do it.'

'Who am I to arrest?' said Mr Goddard, 'I don't know any murderers. I don't so much as know the name of a single murderer. If I did, I'd be off after him at once.'

'Who is he to arrest, Miss Blow?' said Lord Manton. 'You'll have to give him the name and address of your murderer. I suppose you know who he is and where he lives.'

'Yes, I do,' said Miss Blow. 'I didn't at first, but now I do.'

Wilkins entered the room as she spoke. 'I beg your pardon, my lord,' he said.

'Yes, Wilkins, what is it? Be as quick as you can, Wilkins. We are at a most interesting point of our conversation. Miss Blow is just going to reveal to us the name of a murderer, and then Mr Goddard is going out to arrest him.'

'I beg pardon, my lord, but the ladies in the big drawing-room have been ringing the bell.'

'Much, Wilkins? I mean to say, have they been ringing it an excessive number of times, or very hard? There is no harm in their ringing moderately. I should wish them to ring when they want anything.'

'They've been ringing a good deal, my lord.'

'Are they still ringing?'

'Yes, my lord. That's the reason I mentioned it. I thought there might be something you would wish me to say to them.'

'Quite right,' said Lord Manton. 'I'm very glad you told me.

My idea would be for you to offer them a cup of tea or something of that sort to keep them quiet. Or what would you say, Miss Blow, if we had them down here? They might take to smashing up the furniture and the ornaments if I keep them there much longer. There's some china in the room that I'd be sorry to lose. Not very valuable, you know, but still things that it would be difficult to replace. Don't tell us the name of your murderer for a minute or two. Mr Goddard and I will restrain our impatience. I'd like the other ladies to be here when you make the revelation. I'm sure they'd enjoy hearing all about it. Wilkins, will you kindly go to the big drawing-room and ask the three ladies to be good enough to come down here?'

18

AFTER a delay of about five minutes Wilkins opened the door of the library again.

'Miss Farquharson, Mrs Sanders, and Mrs Dick,' he announced, giving the names in the order in which he had received them from Miss Farquharson, who had taken command of the party.

She entered the room first. Her face was pale with anxiety. Her manner and expression were those of a woman who was very much in earnest. Her hat, a severe garment of grey felt adorned with a single bow of black ribbon, was pushed to one side of her head. Her hair, hurriedly pinned into place early in the morning, was untidy. She looked as if she had been working so hard as to have had scant leisure for attention to the details of her toilet. Mrs Dick followed her. She was tremulous and showed signs of having wept frequently and bitterly during the earlier part of the day. Mrs Sanders, a sallow, lean woman of about five and thirty, seemed frightened and bewildered.

'I hope,' said Miss Faquharson, 'that we are not intruding on you. Our business is really very important. That must be our excuse.'

'Not in the least,' said Lord Manton. 'We are all delighted to see you. As a matter of fact, you couldn't have come at a more appropriate moment. Miss Blow is just—but won't you sit down? You'll be much more comfortable sitting down.'

He pulled a chair forward towards Mrs Dick, who collapsed into it and took out her pocket-handkerchief. Mrs Sanders perched herself uncomfortably on a corner of the sofa. Miss Farquharson sat upright in the writing-chair which stood in front of Lord Manton's desk.

'Miss Blow,' said Lord Manton, 'is just going to tell us the name of the man who has murdered your husbands.'

Mrs Dick gave a queer cry, half wail, half whoop, a loud cry, ending in a gasp.

'Murdered!' she cried. 'Murdered! Oh no, no, not murdered!'

'Certainly not murdered,' said Lord Manton. 'That's only what Miss Blow says. I don't believe they're murdered. Neither does Mr Goddard, and if anybody knows the ins and outs of this unfortunate business it's Mr Goddard. He's a policeman, the chief policeman of this district. It stands to reason that he must know. Don't be the least uneasy, ladies. There's no necessity for tears. Nobody is murdered.'

Mrs Dick allowed herself to be a little comforted by this strong assurance. She stopped making any very loud noise and let her crying subside into a subdued and inoffensive whimper. On the other hand, Miss Blow was evidently enraged by Lord

Manton's scepticism. Her voice, when she spoke, sounded defiant and extremely angry.

'I denounce the inhabitants of the house called Rosivera,' she said, 'especially the man Red. I denounce them as the murderers of Dr O'Grady, Patrick Devlin, and of the husbands of these ladies.'

'Go,' said Lord Manton to Mr Goddard, 'and arrest the man Red at once.'

He liked the phrase 'the man Red'. It sounded as if it came out of a newspaper report of a criminal trial. It was evident that Miss Blow had a feeling for appropriate expression.

'Arrest the man Red,' repeated Lord Manton, seeing that Mr Goddard had not moved.

He was perfectly willing that Mr Red should be arrested, tried, imprisoned, hanged; or arrested, imprisoned, and hanged without a trial, on a charge of murder or any other charge. The really important thing was not to obtain justice for Mr Red or anybody else, but to get Miss Blow out of his house.

'Do go and arrest the man Red, Goddard,' he said again.

'I can't,' said Mr Goddard. 'How can I possibly go and arrest a man without a single scrap of evidence against him?'

'You hear what he says,' said Lord Manton to Miss Blow. 'He won't act without evidence. Why don't you produce your evidence? You have evidence, of course.'

'You shall hear the evidence,' said Miss Blow. 'I have evidence that four, if not five abominable murders have been committed by this man and his confederates.'

'There now, Goddard,' said Lord Manton, 'what more can you want? Good gracious, what's that?'

It was Mrs Dick. Miss Blow's last words had been too much for her. She was uttering a series of wild shrieks. Mrs Sanders was sobbing convulsively on the sofa.

'We'll have to go into another room,' said Lord Manton, 'to hear the evidence.'

184

'No,' said Miss Farquharson. 'Now we are here we'll stay here. I am anxious to hear what this lady has to say.'

'But,' said Lord Manton, 'we can't possibly hear anything while——'

Miss Farquharson approached Mrs Dick, grasped her two hands, and spoke sternly to her. She repeated the treatment with her niece. It was most efficacious. Both the younger ladies seemed to be afraid of Miss Farquharson. They had a cowed, terrified look when she left them; but they had stopped making a noise.

'Thank you,' said Lord Manton. 'Now, Miss Blow.'

'I begin,' said Miss Blow, 'with the two latest cases. These gentlemen, Members of Parliament, as I understand, set out on their bicycles, to ride to Pool-a-donagh. They did not arrive there. They were seen in safety three miles out of Clonmore by a man who was carting turf.'

'How do you know that?' said Mr Goddard.

'The hotel-keeper told me,' said Miss Blow.

'Oh, Jimmy O'Loughlin! I see. I wouldn't take every word he says for gospel if I were you, Miss Blow.'

'I don't see,' said Miss Blow, 'that there's much difference between him and the rest of you. I haven't heard six consecutive words of truth since I came to Clonmore.'

'There you are now, Goddard,' said Lord Manton. 'That's what you get by interrupting. Don't mind him. Miss Blow. Please go on. What you say is most interesting.'

'There is just one house between the spot at which they were seen and Pool-a-donagh,' said Miss Blow. 'The hotel-keeper told me that too.'

'I think that's true,' said Miss Farquharson. 'I noticed that there were very few houses while we drove along yesterday.'

'Therefore,' said Miss Blow, 'they were murdered in that house.'

Mr Goddard started violently. The sequence of Miss Blow's reasoning had the effect of a strong electric shock on him. He would have protested if Mrs Dick had not begun to wail again. When she was pacified by Miss Farquharson's scowls, Lord Manton began to speak.

'Perhaps——' he said.

'I know what you're going to say,' said Miss Blow. 'You are going to suggest that they are not murdered, but that they have deserted their wives.' She glanced at Miss Farquharson as she spoke.

'I wish you wouldn't talk of us as if we were all their wives,' said Miss Farquharson. 'I am not a married woman. I am Mr Sanders' aunt. That is his wife.'

She pointed to the pale Mrs Sanders, leaving Miss Blow to infer that the lady who shrieked was the wife of the other Member of Parliament.

'That they have deserted these ladies,' said Miss Blow, accepting the correction, 'because they wear red dressing-gowns, and——'

'But I don't,' wailed Mrs Dick, 'I've never had a red dressing-gown. Richard always liked me in blue. He couldn't bear red. He used to say——Oh, poor Richard!'

'There!' said Lord Manton, with an air of triumph; 'what did I tell you, Miss Blow? You see for yourself now that the man had the strongest possible objection to a red dressing-gown.'

'And,' said Miss Blow firmly, ignoring the interruptions, 'because they washed their teeth. '

'I never in my life,' said Miss Farquharson, 'heard such a pack of nonsense. Are you all mad, or am I? What on earth have red dressing-gowns or that unfortunate little Mrs Dick's teeth got to do with the disappearance of my nephew and Mr Dick?'

'Shall I ring for some tea?' said Lord Manton. 'I think we'd all be the better of a cup of tea. Then we could go on. We'd be much better able to understand each other afterwards.'

'I pass on to the next case,' said Miss Blow calmly; 'that of Patrick Devlin. He is, I am informed——'

'Jimmy O'Loughlin again,' said Mr Goddard.

'By others as well as the hotel-keeper,' said Miss Blow, showing that she placed no implicit trust in Jimmy O'Loughlin's statements. 'I am informed that he is a blacksmith. He was, it appears, collecting money for some local sports.'

'Grand Annual Regatta and Horse Races,' said Lord Manton. 'I'm a member of the committee, and so I know. Please excuse me interrupting you, Miss Blow, but in a case like this it's as well to be perfectly accurate.'

'He informed the hotel-keeper in Clonmore——' said Miss Blow.

'I propose,' said Mr Goddard, 'that we send down for Jimmy O'Loughlin, and let him give his evidence himself.'

'That he intended to call on Lord Manton for a subscription and then go on to Rosivera to see what he could get from the man Red. Did he call here?'

'Certainly,' said Lord Manton. 'I gave him a sovereign.'

'After that,' said Miss Blow, 'he was seen no more. It seems to me perfectly obvious that he went on to Rosivera and was there murdered.'

Poor Mrs Dick wailed again, and was again suppressed, this time very rapidly, by Miss Farquharson.

'There remains,' said Miss Blow, 'the case of Dr O'Grady; but before I go into that I have to inform you that there is another man missing.'

'My goodness!' said Lord Manton. 'The thing is becoming a perfect epidemic. Who is it now?'

'Jimmy O'Loughlin, I hope and trust,' said Mr Goddard. 'He's been dragged into this business by everybody that has said anything. It's always Jimmy O'Loughlin told me this or Jimmy O'Loughlin told me that. If he's gone off himself now it serves him jolly well right.'

'It's not Mr O'Loughlin,' said Miss Blow, 'but the man Red's own servant, an Englishman. This man used to drive the motor car into Clonmore to do the marketing for the party at Rosivera.'

'At Jimmy O'Loughlin's shop, of course,' said Mr Goddard.

'He did so for the last time the day before Dr O'Grady's disappearance. The inference is perfectly plain. The man was mortally wounded. Dr O'Grady was decoyed to Rosivera because his services as a medical man were required. Then he too, to secure his silence, was foully murdered.'

Mr Goddard gasped. For the second time Miss Blow's logic took away his breath. He tried to speak, but failed. Three times he got as far as uttering the word 'but' and then stuck fast. Lord Manton, who remained comparatively calm, offered a mild criticism.

'There is just one point,' he said, 'in the course of your extremely able and lucid statement, on which I should like to have a word of explanation. I have no doubt that you have thought the matter out carefully, and will be able to meet my difficulty at once. You say—and of course I don't contradict you—that Mr Red, I mean the man Red, of course, first tried to murder his own servant and then sent for Dr O'Grady to cure him. Now, why should a man get a doctor for the person he's trying to kill? Wouldn't it have been simpler—I mean to say, do murderers generally summon medical assistance for their victims?'

'I am not concerned with his reasons for acting as he did,' said Miss Blow. 'I am dealing simply with what has occurred, with plain facts. Now, perhaps, you will do your duty, Mr Goddard, and arrest the murderers.'

'But,' said Mr Goddard, 'you haven't given us any evidence at all. You've spun out a lot of wild hypotheses, supported by information given you by Jimmy O'Loughlin, who is the biggest liar in Connacht. It's perfectly absurd to suppose——'

'I join with this lady,' said Miss Farquharson, 'with this lady whose name, as I understand, is Miss Blow, in demanding the arrest of the suspected persons.'

'Oh no, no,' wailed Mrs Dick. 'Don't arrest them. Let us forgive them; but bring Richard back to me. It's cruel, cruel. I can't live—oh, I can't——'

Her voice died away to a whisper. Miss Farquharson was gazing at her with a very stern expression.

'I can't,' said Mr Goddard, 'and won't allow myself to be hustled into a perfectly illegal act. The thing's——'

'You'll have to do it sooner or later,' said Lord Manton. 'Why not do it at once? After all, what does it matter about the man Red? It won't do him any harm to be arrested. If he doesn't deserve it for murdering Dr O'Grady and the rest of them, he's sure to deserve it for something else that we know nothing about.'

'I'm not thinking about Mr Red's feelings in the matter. I don't care if he's hanged, drawn, and quartered, so long as Miss Blow does it herself. But I'm not going to be dragged into a——'

'Look here,' said Lord Manton in a whisper, 'you must do it, Goddard. If you don't, I shall never get these ladies out of the house.'

'Very well,' said Mr Goddard, 'I'll do it; but I'll do it on your authority. Make out a warrant in proper form and sign it. Then I'll go and arrest Red.'

'Certainly,' said Lord Manton. 'I haven't got the—ah—the necessary papers here, you know. I don't keep them in the house. Go down to the Clerk of Petty Sessions, Miss Blow. You'll find him in his office. Get him to fill the form in the proper way. He'll understand. Then send it up to me by one of the police. I'll sign it and hand it on to Mr Goddard. I think that will be the most satisfactory arrangement we can make. Don't you?'

He appealed to Miss Farquharson, carefully avoiding Miss Blow's eye.

'Certainly,' said Miss Farquharson. 'Everything ought to be done in a strictly legal manner.'

'Then I suppose,' said Lord Manton, 'that our interview is at an end. Shall I order the carriage, Miss Blow, to take you down to Clonmore? It will save time.'

'It would be very kind of you to do so,' said Miss Farquharson. 'I am quite able and willing to walk, but my niece and Mrs Dick are upset and greatly tired.'

I shall stay here,' said Miss Blow; 'I shall not let Lord Manton out of my sight till the warrant is signed.'

Miss Farquharson started. This expression of want of faith in the good will of a peer shocked her. She expostulated with Miss Blow, but without effect.

'I shall then go with Mr Goddard,' said Miss Blow, 'and see that he executes the warrant.'

'Really,' said Miss Farquharson, 'I don't understand—I altogether refuse to associate myself with this discourteous language.'

'I know these gentlemen,' said Miss Blow, 'and you don't. I've had some experience of the way they keep their promises.'

'I dissociate myself entirely——' said Miss Farquharson.

'I appreciate Miss Blow's feeling,' said Lord Manton. 'I quite understand it. I even sympathize with it. There has been a good deal in Mr Goddard's conduct during the last few days which justifies her suspicions. I——'

'And in your own conduct,' said Miss Blow.

'And in my own conduct, of course,' said Lord Manton. 'Didn't I say that? I meant to. We have acted for the best. You, at least, will believe that, Miss Farquharson. If Miss Blow has not fully realized our difficulties, that is not her fault. I don't in the least blame her for the attitude she has taken up. Nor does Mr Goddard.'

Mr Goddard looked as if he did blame her, but he said nothing. The swift glances of appeal which Lord Manton shot at him were sufficient to keep him silent.

'What I propose now,' said Lord Manton, 'is that Mr Goddard and I should accompany you to the village, so that Miss Blow shall have the opportunity of seeing with her own eyes that her wish with regard to the man Red is carried out.'

'That will be giving you far too much trouble,' said Miss Farquharson.

'Not at all,' said Lord Manton. 'I'm delighted to do it. Mr

Goddard, the bell is just beside you; will you be so good as to ring it? I shall order the waggonette to take us down. And I think you must allow me to offer you some tea. You can drink it while the horses are being harnessed, and so waste no time.'

'It's very kind of you,' said Miss Farquharson, 'most kind; we shall be very glad——'

'I shall neither eat nor drink in this house,' said Miss Blow.

'I quite understand your feeling,' said Lord Manton. 'There was a prophet once who said the same thing. As well as I recollect, a lion ate him afterwards; but of course that won't happen in your case, Miss Blow. There aren't any lions in Connacht.'

'*I*,' said Miss Farquharson, with strong emphasis on the pronoun, 'shall be very pleased to accept Lord Manton's hospitality in the spirit in which it is offered.'

'Thank you,' said Lord Manton. 'And I'm sure Miss Blow won't have the least objection to your doing so. She holds her own opinions, as we all do; but from what I know of her I'm convinced that she doesn't want to force them upon other people.'

'It is understood,' said Miss Blow, 'that I accompany Mr Goddard when he goes to arrest the murderers.'

'He may not go himself,' said Lord Manton. 'You will understand, Miss Blow, that it is not usual for a man in Mr Goddard's position, for an officer, to make arrests in person. It is probable that he will send Sergeant Farrelly and perhaps one of the constables.'

'I shall accompany the sergeant, then,' said Miss Blow.

19

—➤◦◦➤—

LORD MANTON'S waggonette was a roomy vehicle, used chiefly for picnic parties in the summer, when Lady Flavia and her children were at Clonmore Castle. The four ladies, Lord Manton, and Mr Goddard packed themselves into it quite comfortably. Lord Manton gave his order to the coachman.

'Down to the village, Thomas, and stop at the hotel.'

Miss Blow was alert and suspicious. 'Why the hotel?' she asked.

'I'll go to the police barrack if you like,' said Lord Manton. 'I only suggested the hotel because it is a convenient central sort of place with a room in it large enough to hold the whole party.'

'The hotel is decidedly the most suitable place,' said Miss Farquharson.

She was beginning to dislike Miss Blow, whose manner struck her as aggressive to a degree quite unsuitable in a young woman. On the other hand, she highly approved of Lord Manton, who was most courteous and had given her tea, which she wanted badly.

'Besides,' said Mr Goddard, 'we shall be sure of seeing Jimmy O'Loughlin at the hotel.'

'I don't see why Mr O'Loughlin should be mixed up in our business,' said Miss Blow.

'Nor do I,' said Mr Goddard. 'I've always protested against the way he's dragged in. But everybody does it. Sergeant Farrelly can't say a simple sentence without quoting Jimmy as his authority; and you did the same thing yourself repeatedly when you were elaborating your theory of murder.'

'Besides,' said Lord Manton, 'Jimmy O'Loughlin is a magistrate. He is really far more of a magistrate than I am.'

'If he's a magistrate,' said Miss Farquharson, 'we ought to consult him.'

'He's a liar,' said Miss Blow definitely.

'Really!' said Miss Farquharson.

Then she turned her back on Miss Blow, who sat next her, and looked with great interest at the horses. Mr Goddard leaned across the waggonette and whispered to Lord Manton.

'What do you mean to do when we get to the hotel?'

'Hush!' said Lord Manton.

Miss Blow's eyes were fixed on him, and he felt that confidences were dangerous.

Jimmy O'Loughlin greeted the party at the door of his hotel. He was surprised to see them. He was still more surprised when Lord Manton demanded the use of a private sitting-room.

'There's the commercial room,' he said, 'and there's the drawing-room. You can have the two of them if you like, for there isn't a soul stopping in the house this minute barring the doctor's young lady. It'll be better, maybe, for you to take the commercial room by reason of there being a key to the door, so as you'll be able to lock it if you heard Bridgy coming along the passage.'

'What are you going to do now?' said Mr Goddard, catching Lord Manton by the arm, as the ladies entered the commercial room.

'I'm going to persuade Jimmy O'Loughlin to sign the warrant, if I possibly can,' said Lord Manton.

'He'll not do it. Jimmy O'Loughlin's not a born fool.'

'Then I'm afraid,' said Lord Manton, 'that you'll have to arrest the man Red without a warrant.'

'I won't,' said Mr Goddard.

'Send the sergeant, then.'

'I won't.'

'Couldn't you send the sergeant and a constable and tell

them to inquire civilly of Mr Red whether he'd seen anything of the Members of Parliament? It's quite a natural thing to ask. They passed his gate yesterday, and he might have seen them. We could give the sergeant some sort of a blue paper in the presence of Miss Blow and pretend that he was going to make the arrest.'

'That's no good,' said Mr Goddard. 'She said she'd go and see the arrest made herself, and she'll do it.'

'Send the men on bicycles', said Lord Manton, 'then she won't be able to keep up with them.'

'The objection to that is that she has a bicycle herself. I don't know how she got it, but she rode over on it from Ballymoy this morning. Moriarty might get ahead of her, but she'd knock spots out of the sergeant in a race; he's fat.'

'Jimmy O'Loughlin,' said Lord Manton, 'come here.'

Jimmy was leaning in a careless attitude against the doorpost of his hotel. He appeared to be entirely uninterested in what was going on, and was surprised when Lord Manton called him.

'Jimmy O'Loughlin,' said Lord Manton, 'Mr Goddard is sending a couple of police over to Rosivera to see if there's any news there of the gentlemen that have got lost, and he doesn't want Miss Blow to go with them. Can you think of any way of stopping her?'

'Her mind's made up to go,' said Mr Goddard.

Jimmy meditated on the problem.

'If so be,' he said at last, 'that I could get the boots off of her, and had them hid in the haggard where she wouldn't find them easy, she couldn't go.'

'She could not,' said Mr Goddard. 'But how do you propose to get them off her?'

'I was thinking,' said Jimmy, 'that if his lordship here would draw down the subject of boots, and was to say that all boots was the better of being cleaned, and then if I was to say that Bridgy was doing nothing particular and would be glad to give a rub to any lady's boots that liked, that maybe she'd take them off herself.'

'If that's the best you can do in the way of a suggestion,' said Mr Goddard, 'you might as well have kept it to yourself. Is it likely she'd take off her boots at this hour of the day to please you?'

'It wouldn't be to please me,' said Jimmy; 'it would be his lordship that would ask her at the latter end.'

'I'm afraid,' said Lord Manton, 'she wouldn't do it for me. She doesn't like me. You'd think she would, but as a matter of fact she doesn't.'

'How would it be,' said Jimmy, 'if I was to have a telegram for her? The young lady that minds the post-office is a niece of my own. It might be in it that it was from the doctor himself and came from New York. That would turn her mind away from the police.'

'She wouldn't believe it,' said Mr Goddard. 'Not if you were to go in and swear to it on a Bible. She says you're an awful liar.'

'Begad, then, I don't know what it would be best to do.'

Sergeant Farrelly, Constable Cole, and Constable Moriarty arrived at the door. They had been summoned by Lord Manton's coachman after he had deposited the party at the hotel. The situation was explained to them by Mr Goddard. Sergeant Farrelly expressed perfect readiness to go to Rosivera and make any inquiries that were considered necessary. When asked whether he could escape without Miss Blow, he looked blank. As a matter of fact, Miss Blow had opened the door of the commercial room and was watching the party in the hall with suspicious eyes.

'Unless,' said Constable Cole, 'we could hit on some kind of a stratagem.'

'You and your stratagems,' said the sergeant; 'we've heard enough of them.'

'If you have a stratagem in your mind,' said Mr Goddard, 'trot it out. But there's no use your suggesting taking her boots, or sending her a bogus telegram. We've discussed those two plans already.'

'Don't you give heed to him,' said the sergeant. 'Stratagems is never out of his mouth, and there's no sense at all in what he says.'

'How would it be,' said Constable Cole, 'if the sergeant and myself was to go off to Rosivera on our bikes?'

'That's been suggested before,' said Mr Goddard, 'and it's no good. She has a bicycle herself, and she'd go with you.'

'Sure he knows she has a bicycle,' said Jimmy O'Loughlin. 'Didn't he see her riding in on it this morning, the time you were off up at the Castle? And didn't he remark on its being mighty like the machine that the sergeant's wife beyond in Ballymoy is after buying?'

'I did,' said Constable Cole.

'If you knew all that,' said Mr. Goddard, 'what on earth was the good of your suggesting that you and the sergeant should go on bicycles? Don't you know she'd be after you?'

'Stratagems!' said Sergeant Farrelly scornfully. 'Do you call them stratagems?'

'How would it be,' said Constable Cole, 'if you was to go in to her and tell her that it was Constable Moriarty that was to go with the sergeant to Rosivera?'

'I dislike telling gratuitous and entirely useless lies,' said Mr Goddard. 'She simply wouldn't believe me.'

'She'd believe Moriarty,' said Cole. 'She has a great wish for Moriarty since the day he took her for a drive on Jimmy O'Loughlin's car. If Moriarty was to go in as soon as ever you were done telling her, and was to say he'd be glad if she'd go along with him——'

'I couldn't say the like to a young lady,' said Moriarty. 'I'd be ashamed.'

'Be quiet, Moriarty,' said Mr Goddard. 'And let's hear the rest of the stratagem.'

'And if he was to say at the same time——' said Cole.

'If who was to say?' asked Lord Manton. 'I'm getting mixed.'

'Constable Moriarty,' said Cole; 'if he was to say that it would be a pleasure to him to go round to the yard and get her bicycle for her the way she'd be ready to go with him and the sergeant——'

'I see,' said Lord Manton.

'She'd go with him to the yard,' said Mr Goddard. 'Don't forget that.'

'She would,' said Cole, 'and on the way there she'd see Moriarty's bicycle and another, as it might be the sergeant's.'

'But of course it wouldn't be the sergeant's,' said Lord Manton.

'It would not. The sergeant and myself might be off by that time a good bit along the road to Rosivera. But the bicycle she'd see would have a look about it as if it might be the sergeant's. It could have his cape strapped on it and maybe his name somewhere about so as she'd notice it.'

'It's just possible,' said Mr Goddard, 'that if she has the sort of confidence you say she has in Moriarty she'll be taken in for five minutes; but at the end of that time she'll be off after you.'

'I wouldn't wonder,' said Cole, 'but the back tyre of her own bicycle might be flat.'

He looked at Jimmy O'Loughlin as he spoke. His face was entirely devoid of any expression, but Jimmy was a man of quick wit.

'Bridgy?' he said.

'Bridgy'd do,' he said.

'Do what?' said Lord Manton. 'I'm getting mixed again.'

'With the blade of a knife?' said Jimmy O'Loughlin.

'That, or a three-pronged fork,' said Cole, 'unbeknown to any but herself.'

'It could be done,' said Jimmy O'Loughlin, 'and Bridgy's the girl for the job.'

'Constable Moriarty,' said Cole, 'would offer to mend it for her, while they'd be waiting for the sergeant, who'd be down at the barrack getting the handcuffs.'

'Oiling them,' said Lord Manton.

'Oiling or such,' said Cole.

'Where's the use of oiling handcuffs?' said the sergeant.

'Shut up, sergeant,' said Mr Goddard. 'That's part of the stratagem.'

'Constable Moriarty,' said Cole, 'would be talking to her pleasant and agreeable the way he'd distract her mind and him mending the tyre. It's himself knows how to talk to a young lady.'

'I do not,' said Moriarty. 'She'd be laughing at me.'

'She'd not laugh,' said Mr Goddard. 'That's one thing you may feel quite sure about. Whatever else she does, she'll not laugh.'

'I'm not fit to talk to her,' said Moriarty.

'You're not fit to mend a tyre either,' said Cole; 'mind that now. When you have the hole there is in it with a patch on it, and you're putting back the cover on the wheel you'd nip the inner tube so as there be a bit took out of it.'

'Do you take me for a fool?' said Moriarty. 'Haven't I mended——'

'I'll take you for a fool,' said Mr Goddard, 'if you don't do exactly what you're told.'

'After that,' said Cole, 'you'll have to mend the tyre again; and I'd say, if you're any kind of good at all, that by the time you've done with it it'll be beyond the help of man in the way of holding the air.'

'It's a great stratagem,' said Lord Manton; 'I never heard a better.'

'It's what I was reading in a book one time,' said Cole. 'You know the book, sergeant——'

'I've heard you speaking about it,' said the sergeant, 'many a time.'

'Well,' said Cole, 'that stratagem was in it. It was a young fellow that was off with a girl that he was wishing to marry and her father was after them. It was bicycles they had. And the young fellow gave half a crown to the man in the hotel to do the like to the old chap's bicycle the way he'd get off with the girl.'

'Whether the idea is absolutely original or not,' said Lord Manton, 'you deserve the greatest credit for applying it to this particular case.'

'It was in my mind,' said Cole, 'and I just said to myself that maybe, if I didn't forget it, it might come in handy some day.'

'At the latter end,' said Moriarty, 'she'll be asking where the sergeant is.'

'At the latter end,' said Mr Goddard, 'when the bicycle's quite past mending, you can tell her that he was obliged to start to Rosivera without her and take Cole along with him.'

'She'll have the face ate off me when I do,' said Moriarty.

'If she does,' said Mr Goddard, 'it won't make much matter to you or any one else. The new one you'll get can't be worse to look at than the one you have.'

'I don't know,' said Sergeant Farrelly, 'how will the sergeant's wife at Ballymoy like having them tricks played with her bicycle. She's a cousin of my own.'

He had never had a high opinion of Cole's stratagems, and it pained him to have to listen to the praise bestowed on this one.

'She can get a new tyre,' said Mr Goddard; 'and serve her jolly well right for lending her bicycle to Miss Blow. She ought to have had more sense.'

A few minutes later Lord Manton and Mr Goddard entered the commercial room of the hotel. They had with them a warrant for the arrest of Theodore Guy Red of Rosivera on a charge of wilful murder. They spread this out on the table and invited Miss Blow to inspect it. She did so, scanning every line carefully.

'It's not signed,' she said.

'No,' said Lord Manton. 'We thought you'd prefer to have it signed in your presence. Kindly ring the bell, Mr Goddard.'

'What for?' said Miss Blow.

'I want a pen and ink for one thing,' said Lord Manton. 'And I want Jimmy O'Loughlin. He's going to sign it too.'

Miss Blow sniffed, but she made no objection to the second signature.

'Now,' said Lord Manton, when he and Jimmy O'Loughlin had signed their names, 'call in the sergeant and the constable.'

Mr Goddard opened the door and summoned the police. They marched into the room and stood upright, rigid and impressive, near the door. They made a great impression on Miss Farquharson. Sergeant Farrelly, in particular, struck her as a kind of embodiment of the spirit of law and order. Mr Goddard held the warrant in his hand and addressed the men.

'Sergeant Farrelly,' he said, 'will take this warrant, proceed at once to Rosivera, and effect the arrest of Theodore Guy Red, the person named in it.'

He looked round as he finished his sentence, and noticed with pleasure that Miss Blow was listening intently to what he said.

'Constable Moriarty,' he went on, 'will accompany the sergeant, and will be prepared to act vigorously in the event of the use of force being necessary to effect the capture of the prisoner.'

He looked round again at Miss Blow. Her face was beginning to assume quite an amiable expression.

'With a view to saving time,' said Mr Goddard, 'the police will proceed to Rosivera on bicycles, starting as soon as possible. Sergeant Farrelly, is your bicycle ready?'

'It is, sir,' said the sergeant. 'It's at the door of the hotel this minute, and my cape is strapped on to the handle bars.'

'Is Constable Moriarty's bicycle ready?' asked Mr Goddard.

'It is, sir,' said the sergeant.

'The police,' said Mr Goddard, 'will be accompanied on this expedition by Miss Blow. Every effort, consistent with the effecting of the arrest, will be made by the police to protect Miss Blow in the event of riot.'

'It will, sir.'

'By the way, Miss Blow,' said Mr Goddard, 'have you got a bicycle?'

'Yes,' said Miss Blow. 'I borrowed one this morning in Ballymoy. It's in the hotel yard now.'

'It's in the stable,' said Jimmy O'Loughlin. 'I'm after telling Bridgy to give it a bit of a rub over with a soft cloth the way it'll be decent like, when the young lady wants it.'

'Sergeant Farrelly,' said Mr Goddard, 'will now proceed to the barrack and provide himself with handcuffs.'

'Carefully oiled,' said Lord Manton.

'He will be accompanied by Constable Cole who will remain on guard at the barrack. Having obtained the handcuffs, Sergeant Farrelly will return to the hotel and join the rest of the party. Constable Moriarty will proceed to the back yard, take Miss Blow's bicycle and wheel it round to the front door, so that everything will be in readiness for an immediate start when Sergeant Farrelly returns with the handcuffs.'

'I can get my bicyle for myself,' said Miss Blow.

'It would be too much trouble for you, miss,' said Jimmy O'Loughlin. 'But of course, if the young lady's doubtful about the way Moriarty might handle it, she's right to go. It's a good bicycle,' he added, 'though I'd say that maybe the back tyre of it was a bit worn.'

Miss Blow, accompanied by Moriarty, who looked extremely uncomfortable, left the room. Sergeant Farrelly and Constable Cole marched rapidly down the street towards the barrack.

'I think, ladies,' said Lord Manton, 'that Mr Goddard and I will leave you for the present. We shall see you this evening again, so we need not say good-bye.'

'That,' said Lord Manton to Mr Goddard as they walked together across the deer park, 'was a good stratagem. I don't altogether envy Moriarty when it comes to its climax; but Cole certainly deserves promotion.'

'I don't see that it's much use in reality,' said Mr Goddard. 'It's only putting off the evil day, you know. When the sergeant comes back from Rosivera we'll have the whole thing to do over again.'

'You told him not to hurry, I hope,' said Lord Manton.

'I told him to spend as long over the job as he possibly could. I told him not to be back before six this evening at the very earliest. But what's the good of that? He's bound to come back some time.'

'Still, it's always so much time gained. We may hear something of the missing men before then. You'll telegraph all over the country of course.'

'I'll go back at once,' said Mr Goddard, 'and take entire possession of the telegram office.'

'Come up and have some luncheon first. The afternoon will be time enough for the telegrams.'

20

THERE are, as Patsy Devlin reminded Jimmy O'Loughlin on the occasion of Miss Blow's first visit to Lord Manton, two ways of getting to the Castle from the village of Clonmore. There is the longer way by the great avenue which leads through the demesne and is remarkable for its fine rows of beech trees. By it all visitors who drive must go. They leave the public road a mile to the east of the village, having passed, supposing them to start from Jimmy O'Loughlin's hotel, both the police barrack and the railway station. There is also the shorter way through the deer park, available only for foot passengers, because it is necessary in the first place to climb a boundary wall. The visitor who goes by this route, supposing once more that he starts from the hotel, leaves the village, and walks in a westerly direction until he comes to the spot where the wall is partially broken down and therefore easy to climb. He passes no building of any importance on his way, because the hotel is almost the last house at the west end of the village street.

When luncheon was over Mr Goddard spoke of going down to Clonmore to send off his telegrams. Lord Manton offered to order the dog-cart and have him driven down. Mr Goddard refused.

'You'd much better let me,' said Lord Manton. 'It will save you a lot of time and do the cob good. He hasn't been out for two days. I've been afraid to put my nose outside the place for fear of meeting the police.'

'I'd like to drive well enough,' said Mr Goddard, 'but I daren't. The fact is, I want to get into the telegraph office without being seen, if possible. Miss Blow is sure to be at the barrack, and I'm a little nervous about passing the door.'

The post-office in Clonmore is a sort of by-product of Jimmy O'Loughlin's commercial activity. The business is carried on in a corner of his shop, and the shop itself is an adjunct of the hotel. Approaching the village from the west you come upon the shop door first, then that of the hotel.

'I dare say you're right,' said Lord Manton. 'Unless Moriarty is a young man with quite remarkable powers of persuasion, Miss Blow's temper is likely to be very bad indeed.'

'She'll find out, of course,' said Mr Goddard, 'that the sergeant really has gone off in the direction of Rosivera, and taken Cole with him. That ought to pacify her to some extent. Still, I think I'll avoid an interview as long as I can.'

By walking through the deer park and approaching the village cautiously, Mr Goddard succeeded in getting into the post-office unseen. After a short search he discovered Jimmy O'Loughlin's niece, a red-haired girl, who sold stamps and sent off and received telegrams. She was indulging in what looked like a flirtation with the station-master, in the millinery department of the shop. Mr Goddard called her away from her companion.

'Susy Lizzie,' he said, 'come here. I want you.'

'Is it stamps?' she asked, 'or is it a postal order?'

'It's neither the one nor the other,' said Mr Goddard; 'it's a telegram. In fact, it's as many telegrams as will keep you busy for the rest of the afternoon, so there won't be any use the station-master waiting for you till you've done.'

Susy Lizzie tossed her head and walked defiantly down the shop to her proper counter. She established herself behind a sort of wire screen and pushed a sheaf of telegraph forms towards Mr Goddard.

'Take those things away,' he said. 'I'm coming inside there to watch you send off my wires and to wait for the answers.'

Susy Lizzie by way of reply drew Mr Goddard's attention to a printed notice which forbade members of the general public entering the inner precincts of the office.

'If you go on with any more of that nonsense,' said Mr Goddard, 'I'll tell your uncle the way I found you this minute with the station-master.'

It was one thing to be bullied by Miss Blow, quite another thing to endure the official insolence of Susy Lizzie. Mr Goddard felt that he was man enough to make a stand against that.

'There'd be nothing to tell if you did,' said Susy Lizzie.

'Wouldn't there? I suppose you'd try and make out he was talking to you about buying a new hat for his mother, and you were showing him the way it ought to be trimmed.'

Susy Lizzie grinned. Then she removed the official notice of no admission, lifted up a slab of her counter, and invited Mr Goddard to enter. The first telegram he handed her completely restored her good humour. It was a message of a delightfully exciting kind.

'To the Inspector-General of Police, Dublin Castle. Your

Members of Parliament are unfortunately lost. Am making inquiries. Goddard, District Inspector.'

After this came eight much longer messages. They were addressed to detective sergeants in Derry, Larne, Belfast, Greenore, Kingstown, Rosslare, and Queenstown. They contained inadequate descriptions of the appearance of Mr Dick and Mr Sanders; and an earnest request that all steamers leaving for American, Scottish, or English ports might be watched. While Susy Lizzie was tapping her way through these messages, Mr Goddard unrolled an ordnance survey map, and made a list of all the railway stations within fifty miles of Clonmore. He then wrote out a series of messages to the police sergeants of these places, directing them to make inquiries at the railway stations about all strangers who had left by train that day. He appended, for the further guidance of the police, his descriptions of the Members of Parliament, and a note to the effect that one of them was riding a lady's bicycle.

Susy Lizzie handed him a reply to his first message.

'From Under Secretary, Dublin Castle, Inspector-General of police in Belfast quelling riot. Wire forwarded. Lord Lieutenant anxious to know whether ladies of party safe.'

Mr Goddard replied at once, 'Ladies perfectly safe, but anxious and tearful.'

Susy Lizzie, by this time in a state of extreme excitement and perfect good temper, set to work again at the seaport messages. She had got as far as Greenore when she had to stop to receive another incoming message.

'From Chief Secretary, Dublin Castle. Please explain first wire. Unintelligible here.'

This was followed immediately by one from Belfast.

'Inspector-General supposes mistake in transmission of wire. Kindly repeat.'

Mr Goddard wrote out two replies.

'To Chief Secretary, Dublin Castle. Members of Parliament completely lost during night. Deeply regret occurrence. Goddard, District Inspector.'

'To Inspector-General of Police, Belfast. First message probably correctly transmitted. Members of Parliament cannot be found. Goddard, District Inspector.'

Susy Lizzie, working at high speed, got these messages despatched and went on with those to Dublin, Kingstown, Rosslare, and Queenstown. Then Mr Goddard handed her a bundle of forms which contained his appeals to the police at the railway stations. He felt that he had done all that could be done to discover the escaped gentlemen. It is impossible, as Mr Goddard knew, to get out of Ireland without going either to Great Britain or America. Derry and Queenstown were the ports of exit westward. If, as was far more likely, the fugitives had made a rush for England or Scotland, he would get news of them at one of the other places. It was possible, of course, that they were still loitering about Ireland. In that case he would hear of them from one of his railway stations. Even the most energetic Member of Parliament would not be likely to do more than fifty miles on his bicycle over west of Ireland roads, and Mr Sanders was afflicted with a weak heart.

'Isn't there some way of getting from the hotel to the shop,' said Mr Goddard, 'without going out into the street? I want to speak to your uncle.'

'There is surely,' said Susy Lizzie. 'If you step across to the grocery counter, the young gentleman that's there will show you the door.'

The door, as Mr Goddard found when the young gentleman opened it for him, led directly to the hotel bar. Jimmy O'Loughlin was serving out bottles of porter to about a dozen customers. There was a babble of talk, which ceased abruptly as Mr Goddard entered.

'Jimmy,' he said, 'I want to speak to you for a minute.'

'Affy Ginnetty,' said Jimmy, 'come here and attend the bar.'

The young gentleman who had opened the door for Mr Goddard left the care of the bacon, flour, and tobacco which strewed his counter, and took his place behind the bar. Jimmy led the way to the ironmongery corner of his shop.

'We'll have this place to ourselves,' he said. 'There's nobody comes to buy them things'—he indicated an assortment of lamps, pots, and rat-traps—'unless it would be of a fair day.'

'Jimmy,' said Mr Goddard, 'where are the ladies?'

'There's two of them,' said Jimmy, 'that's in their beds.'

'I suppose it's in them they are. Anyway, they said they were going to lie down, and Bridgy brought up a can of hot water apiece for them, and I didn't see them since. There was talk,' he added, 'of their being up and dressed again to be down ready at the barrack at four o'clock, that being the hour at which they were expecting Sergeant Farrelly to be back.'

'Those,' said Mr Goddard, 'are probably Mrs Dick and Mrs Sanders.'

'They might be.'

'And what about the other two?'

'There's one of them that's writing letters above in the drawing-room. She sent Bridgy for two-pennyworth of paper and envelopes, and I gave her the loan of a bottle of ink and a writing pen. I heard her say she'd be down along with the other two at the barrack at four o'clock to see the sergeant.'

'That's most likely to be Miss Farquharson.'

'I wouldn't say,' said Jimmy, 'whether the sergeant would be back at four.'

'He will not, nor yet at five.'

'I was thinking as much.'

'Where's Miss Blow?'

'The doctor's young lady,' said Jimmy, 'is down at the barrack along with Moriarty.'

'I'm glad to hear that.'

'She wasn't as much put out as you'd expect,' said Jimmy, 'when she found she couldn't go on the bicycle. I was thinking she might be in a bad way and that maybe she'd be too much for Moriarty, so I sent Bridgy into the yard to her, not caring to go myself——'

'You were right there,' said Mr Goddard.

'Bridgy told me after, that she never saw in all her born

days anything to equal the state that Moriarty had the tyre in "You could have run the wisps of it," she said, "through the teeth of a fine comb." '

'Get Bridgy,' said Mr Goddard. 'I'd like to hear the story from herself.'

'I'm not sure could I get her, for she's busy with the pig's food and would be wanting to clean herself before she'd come. But there's no need anyway, for I can tell you the way she quietened the doctor's young lady as well as she'd tell it herself, and maybe better, for she might be backward in speaking out before a gentleman. "The sergeant bid me say," says Bridgy, "that he's off this quarter of an hour, and has took Constable Cole along with him." Only for Moriarty being there and listening to her Bridgy says the young lady would have cursed awful at hearing that. "Wild horses," says Bridgy, "wouldn't have held the sergeant back from going, he was that set on catching the blackguards that ill-treated the poor doctor." Bridgy says the young lady seemed more pacified at them words. "The sergeant," says Bridgy, "is a terrible man when his temper is riz, and riz it is this day if ever it was. I'd be sorry for the man that faces him." And so she went on telling stories about the sergeant and Constable Cole that would make you think they were the blood-thirstiest villains in Ireland, and that nothing delighted them only getting a hold of murderers and the like.'

'And did Miss Blow believe all that?'

'I'm not sure did she, but it quietened her. She didn't say a word to Moriarty, good nor bad, but she went out into the street and she asked the first three men she met where was Sergeant Farrelly and Constable Cole.'

'Well, and what did they tell her?'

'They told her the truth, of course. They told her they'd seen the sergeant and Cole going off on their bicycles back west in the direction of Rosivera. I'm thinking that after that she began to be of opinion that there was, maybe, some truth in what Bridgy had been saying. Anyway, she went off down to the barrack, and Moriarty after her, and she's there yet.'

Susy Lizzie emerged from behind the wire screen of the post-office counter while Jimmy O'Loughlin was speaking. She held in her hand a bundle of telegraph forms. Her uncle caught sight of her.

'What is it you're wanting, Susy Lizzie?' he said. 'Why wouldn't you stay where you're paid to stay and attend to the wants of the public?'

'It's a dozen wires and more,' said Susy Lizzie, 'that's after coming for Mr Goddard, and I thought maybe he'd like to get them at once.'

'You thought right,' said Mr Goddard. 'Hand them over.'

The first he looked at was from Derry.

'Two men, answering the description given, but without bicycles, left this night at eight P.M., on steamer *Rose* for Glasgow. Have wired Chief of Police there.'

'That'll hardly be them,' said Jimmy O'Loughlin, who was looking over Mr Goddard's shoulder.

'It can't possibly be them,' said Mr Goddard. 'I defy them to get from this to Derry between twelve o'clock yesterday and eight in the evening. I hope to goodness those silly asses won't go and arrest two total strangers and dump them down on us here. We have worry enough without that.'

'I don't know, said Jimmy, 'if so be the men they got were decent sort of men, it might be——'

'What's that you're saying?' said Mr Goddard.

He had glanced at five more telegrams which came from the police who lived in towns where trains stopped. They all denied any knowledge of the Members of Parliament.

'I was saying,' said Jimmy, 'that maybe since the gentlemen that's wanted can't be found, the ones they'd be sending over to us from Glasgow might be some comfort to the ladies. Susy Lizzie, what are you doing standing there with a grin on your face that a man could post a letter through? Aren't you ugly enough the way God made you without twisting the mouth that's on you into worse than it is? Get back with you and mind the telegraph machine. I hear it ticking away there as if the devil was in it. Be off with you now, and don't let me be obliged to speak to you twice. I was saying, Mr Goddard——'

'I heard what you were saying,' said Mr Goddard, 'and I never heard greater nonsense in my life.'

He was scattering more pink papers on the floor as he spoke. Every railway station about which he inquired had been drawn blank.

'Do you suppose,' he went on, 'that a lady like Mrs Dick, who has been crying the whole day because she's lost her husband, would take up straight off with any strange man the police happened to send her over from Glasgow? Have some sense, Jimmy.'

'It's them ones that cries the most,' said Jimmy, 'that is the quickest to get married again if so be there's anybody willing to take them.'

'I don't deny that,' said Mr Goddard; 'but, hang it all! You must give her time to make sure that the first one's really dead. I don't believe he is myself. Damn it all! Look at this!'

He held out a telegram, the last of his batch, to Jimmy O'Loughlin.

'From Inspector-General of Police. Matter of disappearance of Members of Parliament serious. Keep news out of papers if possible. Am leaving Belfast tonight. Shall reach Clonmore tomorrow noon. Meet train and report.'

'I don't know,' said Jimmy, 'will he be expecting to stay the night at the hotel, for if he is there's no place for him to sleep. There's the doctor's young lady has the big front room, and yourself and the other three ladies has all the rest of the bed-rooms there is in it, and the like of a high-up man such as the Inspector-General will be looking for something better than a sofa in the drawing-room. I don't know either is Bridgy fit to cook the sort of dinner he'd be accustomed to.'

'I don't care a straw where he sleeps. What I'm thinking

about is the abominable fuss there'll be when he arrives. One comfort is he won't be able to find these wretched Members of Parliament any more than I can myself.'

'He might, then,' said Jimmy hopefully.

'He will not; but I tell you what he'll do. He'll find out about the doctor being gone and Patsy Devlin. Then he'll come to the conclusion that there's some sort of a conspiracy on foot in the country. He'll draft in a lot of extra police, and he'll have the life worried out of me. Look here, Jimmy, I can't stand much more of this sort of thing today. You'll have to keep those women off me somehow. I'll count on you to do it. I shall go and shut myself up in the telegraph office along with Susy Lizzie, and if you let one of them in on me I'll never forgive you. Let them fight it out with Sergeant Farrelly when he gets back. Let Cole try them with another stratagem if he likes. All I ask is to have them kept off me.'

'I'll do the best I can,' said Jimmy; 'and if you send Susy Lizzie into the hotel any time, Bridgy'll give her a cup of tea for you. You'll be wanting it.'

2 1

AT four o'clock Miss Farquharson, Mrs Dick and Mrs Sanders went down to the police barrack. They found Miss Blow seated by herself in the men's day room. Constable Moriarty was digging potatoes in the garden at the back of the house. He had been questioned and cross-questioned by Miss Blow for more than an hour after he had completed the destruction of the bicycle tyre. He felt jaded and nervous. He stood on the brink of a frightful exposure. A trifling accident, an incautious word, might at any moment betray the part he had played in Constable Cole's stratagem. Some men under the circumstances would have steadied themselves with whisky, but Moriarty was a strict teetotaller. Others would have smoked pipe after pipe of strong tobacco. Moriarty, much wiser, went out and dug potatoes. There is nothing more soothing to racked nerves than digging in the ground, and there is a mild excitement about driving a spade into potato ridges which distracts the mind from painful thoughts and terrifying anticipations. The turning up of the roots of any particular plant may display an amazing wealth of tubers, may expose to the gaze of the delighted gardener some potato of huge size or very unusual shape. You cannot tell beforehand what will be unearthed. Expectations and hope run high. There is also present a certain fear. It is always possible, unless you are very skilful at the work, that a spade may slice a potato, leaving you face to face with two reproachful, earth-soiled, flat surfaces, useless for the pot, a manifest disgrace to your digging. Moriarty was not a highly skilled or very experienced potato digger. He enjoyed to the full the pleasures of anticipation. He suffered from the bitterness which follows mistakes. He almost forgot Miss Blow and the torment of her questioning.

Then, at a quarter past four, Miss Blow's voice brought him back from his security. She called him by name from the back door of the barrack. Moriarty scraped the clay off the sides of his boots, shuffled on his coat, and gave his hands a rub on the front part of the legs of his trousers. Then he joined Miss Blow and the other ladies in the day room.

'Why isn't Sergeant Farrelly back?' asked Miss Blow.

'I don't know, miss.'

'It's after four,' said Miss Blow.

'Well, now,' said Moriarty, 'that's a queer thing, so it is.'

'He started, I am told, at about half-past twelve.'

'It might have been that,' said Moriarty, 'or it might have

been more. I didn't take notice on account of being engaged in mending your tyre at the time.'

'It's eight miles to Rosivera. Allow three-quarters of an hour to get there——'

'It could be,' said Moriarty, 'that he was punctured on the way. It's a bad road.'

'Allowing for all possible accidents, even supposing he walked the whole way there and back, they should be here by this time.'

'They should. You're right there, miss. They should.'

'Will you,' said Miss Blow. 'kindly go and fetch Mr Goddard, your officer? He ought to know that his men have not returned.'

'I don't know will I be able to find him.'

'Go and try.'

'I will,' said Moriarty. 'I'll go and ask Jimmy O'Loughlin. If anybody knows where the officer is, it'll be Jimmy O'Loughlin.'

Jimmy O'Loughlin told Moriarty to go back to the ladies and keep them amused for a while by showing them over the barrack. Moriarty refused to do this. He said that the situation was urgent and critical, and that he would not take the responsibility of dealing with Miss Blow without help. Jimmy O'Loughlin reluctantly went down to the barrack. Miss Blow attacked him at once.

'Where is Mr Goddard?' she said.

'He's beyond,' said Jimmy, 'in the post-office, and he left word that he wasn't to be disturbed on account of his being terrible busy.'

'He ought to be told that his men have not returned from the Rosivera.'

'I'd be in dread to go near him. It's telegrams he's sending, telegrams to the Lord Lieutenant and more of them high-up gentlemen, and that's the kind of work that would be preying upon a man.'

'Sergeant Farrelly left this at a quarter past twelve,' said Miss Blow; 'and he's not back yet.'

'It's a long road,' said Jimmy, 'longer maybe than you'd think.'

'It's eight miles.'

'And eight back along with that.'

'That only makes sixteen,' said Miss Farquharson, who shared her nephew's fondness for intricate calculations.

'So they ought to be here by this time,' said Miss Blow.

'It could be,' said Jimmy, 'that they might be a long time looking for the gentleman they're after before they'd find him. A fellow like that would be as cunning as an old fox, hiding himself when he saw the police after him.'

'Oh,' said Mrs Dick, 'I do hope nothing has happened to them. It would be too terrible.'

'The sergeant,' said Jimmy, 'is a heavy man. He wouldn't be as quick as another at doing a run on a bicycle.'

'Still,' said Miss Blow, 'he's had four hours and it's only sixteen miles.'

'He'll have to walk back,' said Jimmy, 'and if so be the prisoner wasn't willing to come with him it might be a long time before he got him along the road, for he wouldn't like to be beating him. He has a kind heart, the sergeant; it's hardly ever you'd see him as much as laying a stick across a child.'

Miss Blow seemed more or less satisfied. The idea of Mr Red driven by threat of violent batoning along a dusty road comforted her. Jimmy O'Loughlin made his escape from the barrack.

He found Mr Goddard scribbling a fresh telegram in the post-office.

'Look at that,' he said, handing a form to Jimmy.

'From Chief Secretary, Dublin Castle. Why have you not reported recovery of Members of Parliament?'

'That's not what I'd call a civil message,' said Jimmy. 'What did you say to him?'

'Susy Lizzie,' said Mr Goddard, 'give your uncle the answer I sent to the last telegram but two.'

Susy Lizzie fumbled among a pile of papers and finally handed one over to Jimmy.

'To Chief Secretary, Dublin Castle. Impossible to report recovery of Members of Parliament with any truth because still at large. Goddard, District Inspector.'

'Be damn,' said Jimmy, 'but you had him there, as neat as ever I seen.'

'He's not satisfied, though. Look at this.'

He handed another form to Jimmy.

'From Chief Secretary, Dublin Castle. Lord Lieutenant requests explanation of disappearance of Members of Parliament.'

'Here's the answer to that,' said Mr Goddard. 'Read it out to your uncle, Susy Lizzie, before you send it off.'

Susy Lizzie grinned broadly.

'Go on,' said Jimmy, 'and do what the gentleman bids you. You've no right to be laughing at the business of the Government.'

'Theory current locally,' read Susy Lizzie, 'that Members of Parliament have deserted their wives and aunt.'

'That'll give him his 'nough of telegraphing for this day anyhow,' said Jimmy. 'I'd like to see the way he'll be rampaging up and down the stairs of the Castle when he gets that. It'll show them fellows that you think mighty little of them anyway, Mr Goddard.'

'How are the ladies getting on?'

'I've quietened them for a bit. They were annoyed on account of Sergeant Farrelly not coming back; but I told them it would take him a long time to be dragging Mr Red along the road by the hair of his head, and I didn't think he'd come without. They'll be all right for another hour, anyway. Will I be going into the hotel and telling Bridgy to fetch you over a cup of tea? It's after five o'clock.'

It was nearly six o'clock before Bridgy came to the shop

with a tray in her hands. She was followed by Affy, the young gentleman from the grocery department, who carried a loaf of bread and a pot of jam. Mr Goddard and Susy Lizzie began a comfortable meal together. They were interrupted twice by telegrams from Dublin, but they did not allow these to trouble them much. A very much more serious interruption was caused by a breathless whisper from Affy to the effect that four ladies were entering the shop. Mr Goddard, carrying his tea-cup with him, concealed himself behind a screen of muffed glass, originally erected by the post-office authorities in order that letters might be sorted out of sight of the public.

'Susy Lizzie,' he whispered, 'run like a good girl and get your uncle. Tell him that the ladies are here, and that he'll have to come at once and pacify them.'

Susy Lizzie ran. She was enjoying her afternoon immensely. The monotony of her life was seldom broken in any way half so agreeable.

'If the thing is to be done, I'll do it,' said Jimmy, when he received the message.

He left his bar and went into the shop. He faced Miss Farquharson, who was asking Affy where Mr Goddard was likely to be found.

'I was thinking, my lady,' said Jimmy, 'that maybe you'd be wanting a bit of supper. What would you say now to a chop, or a couple of rashers and some eggs? I could have got them for you in a minute.'

'I want Mr Goddard, the police officer,' said Miss Blow, who stood beside the post-office counter.

'Wouldn't it be better for you now,' said Jimmy, turning to her, 'to be eating your supper quietly instead of rampaging about the town frightening the wits out of a poor man that's doing his best for you? Come now, sure I'm old enough to be your father, and I know what's good for you. It's moidered you are with the trouble that's on you, and there isn't one in the place but is sorry for you and for all the rest of the ladies this night. But what's the good of making yourselves sick over it, and tormenting the officer? If they're gone, they're gone, and all the talking in the world won't bring them back to you.'

'Man——' said Miss Blow.

'Look at poor Susan Devlin,' said Jimmy, 'she's lost a husband as well as the rest of you, and barring that she might be crying an odd time when she'd be thinking of him, she's as quiet as a lamb. Why can't you behave yourselves like her? I'm not setting up to teach ladies like yourselves what ought to be and what ought not, but I'd say myself that the men that would run away from yez, from the like of yez'—he spoke with a smile that was meant to flatter—'isn't worth looking after.'

'Do you dare to suggest——' said Miss Farquharson.

'It's not the first time that suggestion has been made,' said Miss Blow. 'It's part of the scandalous conspiracy in which every man, woman and child in this place is involved.'

'If you won't take your supper when it's offered you,' said Jimmy, 'maybe you'll sit inside in the hotel. You're interrupting the business of the shop standing where you are, let alone preventing the public from having the stamps they have a right to buy to put on their letters.'

The appeal produced its effect on Miss Blow. She had the blood of a business man in her veins. She understood that her father would have resented any interference with the sale of his twopenny Beauties, and would not have admitted either grief or anger as legitimate reasons for damming the flow of trade. Also she and her companions belonged to a law-abiding race. They had a natural respect for any department of the State. They felt it wrong to stop the sale of postage stamps. They trooped into the hotel and sat down in the commercial room. Once there Miss Farquharson's strong common sense asserted itself. She suggested that it might be wise after all to order bacon and eggs, quoting the advice given by St Paul to the sailors who were threatened with shipwreck. Mrs Dick and Mrs Sanders declared with tears that it was impossible for them to eat in their heart-broken condition. This confirmed

Miss Farquharson in her resolve to have a regular meal. She gave the necessary order to Jimmy O'Loughlin. Miss Blow agreed to eat on condition that the meal was served in the commercial room, the windows of which looked out on the street. She knew that Sergeant Farrelly, Constable Cole, and the prisoner must pass the hotel on their way to the barrack.

22

At eight o'clock Mr Goddard, who had enjoyed some fried bacon and a little bottle of porter in the telegraph office, began to feel surprised at the prolonged absence of Sergeant Farrelly. It was all very well to go slowly to Rosivera and to return without undue hurry, but it was hard to imagine how eight hours could possibly be occupied in travelling sixteen miles. He sent Susy Lizzie, who remained in attendance on him, to call her uncle.

'I'm doing the best I can,' said Jimmy, 'to keep them quiet; but they'll be out after you in spite of me soon. I left herself and Bridgy talking to them; but what use are they against the four? And the doctor's young lady is the worst of them.'

'It's not the ladies I'm bothered about now,' said Mr Goddard. 'Why the devil isn't Sergeant Farrelly back? What's keeping him?'

'Faith, I don't know, unless maybe he'd be in dread!'

'Nonsense. I told him not to hurry, but I didn't tell him to stay out all night.'

'It's queer, so it is,' said Jimmy. 'What would you think

now of sending Constable Moriarty out a bit along the road to look and see if there's e'er a sign of them coming?'

'I'll go myself,' said Mr Goddard.

'I wouldn't say,' said Jimmy, 'but what it might be just as well if you did. The ladies is sure to be here in a couple of minutes now. I can't keep them.'

Mr Goddard walked a mile along the road towards Rosivera, and then sat down on a ditch. There was no sign of Sergeant Farrelly. At nine o'clock he got up, and walked another mile and sat down again. Still there was no sign of the missing policeman. He walked a third mile and once more waited. He was puzzled and began to feel uneasy. He turned and walked back towards Clonmore. Half a mile outside the town he climbed the demesne wall and crossed an angle of the deer park to the Castle. It was a quarter past ten when he reached the door.

He found Lord Manton in the library with a book in his hand and a glass of whisky and soda water on the arm of his chair. There was a pile of cigarette ends on the tray which stood within reach.

'Well, Mr Goddard,' he said, 'I suppose you've tucked all your ladies up in bed and come up here for a quiet smoke. You deserve it.'

'No,' said Mr Goddard; 'I've come to consult you. I don't understand——'

'Surely nobody else has bolted?'

'Sergeant Farrelly and the constable have not returned from Rosivera.'

'Dear me! I always heard that these things were infectious, like measles. One suicide, half a dozen suicides. We appear to be in for an epidemic of bolting. But I'd never have suspected the sergeant. He seemed such a solid sort of man, not the least hysterical; but you can never tell. I hope you won't vanish tomorrow, Goddard. If you feel it coming on you, you'd better put yourself under arrest at once. Was the sergeant a married man?'

'No, he wasn't.'

'Then there'll be no widow to make lamentation in his case. That's a good job for you, Goddard. I don't see how you could have got on with another woman running round after you. What about the constable?'

'He's not married either. He's not long enough in the service.'

'Poor fellow!' said Lord Manton. 'I suppose now that this will ruin his prospects, even if he comes back.'

'Lord Manton,' said Mr Goddard, 'what do you know about that tenant of yours at Rosivera?'

'Surely you're not coming round to Miss Blow's murder theory, are you?'

'I don't know. It's a very queer business. Is Red—that's the man's name, isn't it—respectable?'

'I don't know. I never saw the man in my life. I know nothing about him except that he paid his rent and came here in a motor car. That looks as if he had money, doesn't it?'

'I don't understand it,' said Mr Goddard. 'The sergeant and Cole certainly went to Rosivera today. I don't see what was to stop them from getting there. They weren't likely to lose their way. They certainly haven't come back.'

'What does Jimmy O'Loughlin say? I suppose you've consulted him.'

'Jimmy thinks,' said Mr Goddard, 'that the sergeant's afraid to come back on account of Miss Blow. But that's all rot, of course.'

'I'm not at all sure that Jimmy's not right. He's a very shrewd man, Jimmy O'Loughlin. I shouldn't wonder a bit——'

'But what the deuce am I to do?'

'I'll tell you what it is,' said Lord Manton. 'We'll make a descent in force on Rosivera tomorrow. You shall conduct all the police you possibly can, fifty of them, if there are fifty available. We'll take all the ladies interested in the matter in my waggonette. Jimmy O'Loughlin and I will accompany the army in the capacity of civil magistrates, each of us armed with a Riot Act and a writ of Habeas Corpus. We'll make that fellow Red sit up if he's been at any games.'

'I really think we'll have to. It seems very absurd. But what else are we to do? I've been harried with telegrams from everybody in Dublin Castle all day. The Inspector-General is coming down here tomorrow, though I don't see what on earth he thinks he'll be able to do.'

'We'll forestall him,' said Lord Manton. 'He can't possibly get here before noon. We'll start at eleven A.M. sharp. We'll have the mystery, whatever it is, probed to its inmost recesses before he gets at it. The whole credit will be yours, Goddard.'

'I'll make any one that likes a present of the credit.'

'In the meanwhile,' said Lord Manton, 'you'd better sleep here. I expect Jimmy O'Loughlin's hotel is pretty well full up.'

'Thanks,' said Mr Goddard. 'The fact is, I don't particularly care about going back to the village tonight.'

'Will they be waiting up for you?'

'They will.'

'Miss Blow,' said Lord Manton, 'is a wonderful woman.'

'She's not bad looking,' said Mr Goddard magnanimously, 'but she's rather——'

'I know what you're going to say—vehement, wasn't that it? A good deal of life force about her? I quite agree with you. Now, what do you think? Supposing it turns out that the man Red has really been up to any kind of tricks; supposing he's engaged in a business of kidnapping dispensary doctors, blacksmiths, Members of Parliament and policemen, for the purpose of shipping them off as slaves to the Sultan of Zanzibar. I don't say for certain that that's exactly what he's doing. I don't know yet. But if he's at anything of the sort it would serve him jolly well right if we made him marry Miss Blow.'

'He wouldn't do it.'

'He might. He seems to be a man of adventurous disposition. If he doesn't like her, we could offer him Miss Farquharson.'

'I should think he'd refuse them both. He'd see Miss Farquharson and he'd be absolutely certain to hear Miss Blow.'

'I think we could put pressure on him,' said Lord Manton. 'In fact, it would be a choice for him between marrying and a criminal prosecution. A man can't kidnap people in this wholesale sort of way without suffering for it. He'll understand that when we put it to him. But you've had an exhausting day, Goddard, and I dare say you'd like to toddle up to bed. Wilkins will leave you whatever you want. We'll have a great time tomorrow, raiding Rosivera.'

23

Miss Blow was very angry when she discovered that Mr Goddard was not in the telegraph office. Nothing Jimmy O'Loughlin said soothed her in the least. He pointed out that the officer's absence was caused by his excessive zeal for the cause they all had at heart; that he had in fact gone in person to investigate the mystery of Rosivera. Miss Blow refused to believe him, and expressed her contempt for habitual liars in plain language.

'If you don't believe me, miss, ask Constable Moriarty, and he'll tell you the same.'

'I shouldn't believe him either,' said Miss Blow; 'and in any case Constable Moriarty is a fool.'

'He was standing by,' said Jimmy, pursuing the subject without regarding the interruption, 'the same as it might be yourself, and he heard every word that passed between us. "Mr Goddard," I says, "them ladies is in a terrible state, and getting worse. It's hardly ever they were able to take the cup of tea I had wetted for them." "I know it, Jimmy," says he; "I know it well; and if cutting off my right hand would be any ease to them I'd do it this minute." "You would," I says, for I knew well the way it was going through him; "but what good would that be? Wouldn't it be better now if you was——" "If I was to what?" says he, catching me up like. "If you was to send Moriarty for a bit of a stroll along the road," I says, "to see could he hear any news of the sergeant." "I'll not do it," says he, looking terribly determined. "I'll not do the like. What's Constable Moriarty but a boy, Jimmy? A boy with maybe a mother breaking her heart after him somewhere. If there's murder going," says he, "it's not Constable Moriarty it'll light on, but myself." "Do you mean that?" says I. "I do," he says; "I mean it; I'll go myself. What murder's done to-night will be done on me, for I'll not take it on my conscience to be the cause of Moriarty's death." "Mr Goddard," says I, "you're a fine man. I'll give it in to you that you're as brave as any one that ever I met; but you'll be taking your sword with you, promise me that now." "I will, Jimmy," says he; "I'll take my sword, and I'm thankful to you for making the suggestion." And with that, miss, he was up and out of the door, and that was the last I seen of him.'

'If you hadn't been telling me lies ever since I've been in Clonmore,' said Miss Blow, 'there'd be some chance of my believing you now.'

'There's a man going past the door of the hotel this minute,' said Jimmy, 'with an ass load of turf that he's after fetching in off the bog. Will you go out now and ask him did he meet Mr Goddard on the road? Maybe you'll believe him when he tells you.'

Miss Blow accepted the challenge. She waylaid the man with the donkey, who proved to be very deaf. She raised her voice and shouted to him. He replied in a low tone. She shouted again, and the man made what seemed a long answer. Miss Blow returned to Jimmy O'Loughlin.

'You've told me the truth for once,' she said ungraciously. 'That man met the officer a mile out of the town on the road to Rosivera.'

Jimmy was generous. He did not attempt to humiliate Miss Blow. He pursued his policy of trying to soothe her. An hour passed. Two hours passed. Even Miss Blow's anger began to give way to anxiety. What if Mr Goddard was himself a victim to the mysterious gang which had already made away with seven men? He might have gone the whole way to Rosivera. He might have fallen into some craftily arranged ambush on the road. Fear laid hold on her heart. Jimmy O'Loughlin, who was a little puzzled but not particularly anxious, seized his opportunity.

'It'll be better for you,' he said, 'to go to your bed, you and the rest of the ladies, where you'll be safe till the morning. You'll hardly be expecting any other man to be going out into the darkness of the night, risking his life maybe, to satisfy you. Not but what there's many a one would do it. I'd do it myself if I saw any good would come out of it.'

Miss Blow and Miss Farquharson consulted together anxiously. This fresh disaster had gone a long way towards cowing them. They were not prepared to insist on the sacrifice of more human life. Mrs Dick wept noisily and unrebuked. Mrs Sanders became very white and her hands trembled.

'You'll be safe in your beds anyway,' said Jimmy. 'You can turn the key in the door of every room in this house barring the one I sleep in myself, for the lock of it is gone wrong on me, and since poor Patsy Devlin went from us there isn't a man about the place fit to settle it.'

'Let us go,' said Mrs Dick, sobbing. 'I want to be somewhere at peace. I don't care—— Oh, poor Richard!'

'You're right, ma'am,' said Jimmy; 'it'll be better for you. I have a dog in the yard that'll bark fit to wake the dead if e'er a one comes near the house during the night; and I'll leave word with Bridgy that she's to waken you in good time if so be anything was to happen; but with the help of God there'll be no need for that.'

'Come,' said Miss Blow at last; 'we can do no more tonight. Let us get some sleep, if any of us are able to sleep.'

24

It was three o'clock in the afternoon of the day which followed their capture, and the two Members of Parliament showed no signs of becoming reconciled to their situation. Mr Sanders grumbled and occasionally swore. Mr Dick passed from bursts of violent rage to fits of lamentation over the desolate condition of Mrs Dick. Dr O'Grady and Patsy Devlin bore with them patiently for a long time. But there are limits to human endurance. After a consultation with Patsy, the doctor undertook to speak seriously to the unreasonably afflicted men. The bearded anarchist who usually attended to the wants of the prisoners, carried off the dinner things. Dr O'Grady pulled Mr Dick's bed out to the middle of the floor.

'Now,' he said, 'sit down on that, the two of you in a row, till I try if I can't talk sense into you.'

'Why,' said Mr Sanders sulkily, 'why should we sit there and be talked to by you?'

'There are two reasons why you should,' said Dr O'Grady. 'The first is because I want to talk to you, and I can do that much more conveniently if you're seated in a row in front of me than if you're scattered about all over the room. Does that satisfy you, or must I give you the second reason?'

'I won't be talked to by you,' said Mr Dick. 'You're in league with the infernal scoundrels who have locked us up here.'

'My good man——' said Mr Sanders.

This pacific form of address produced no more effect on Dr O'Grady than Mr Dick's blunt denunciation did. Mr Sanders was given no time to finish his remark.

'The second reason why you should is because it will be the worse for you if you don't.'

'Do you mean to threaten us with violence?' said Mr Dick.

'Patsy,' said Dr O'Grady, 'take off your coat, roll up your sleeve and show your arm. I may mention, gentlemen, that Patsy Devlin was a blacksmith by trade before he took to being a captive. He's used to hammering.'

Mr Dick and Mr Sanders watched Patsy Devlin bare his arm, but they made no move towards the bed.

'Patsy,' said Dr O'Grady, 'roll up your other sleeve. If you want to fight, gentlemen, I'd recommend you to take off your coats.'

'I can't fight,' said Mr Sanders, 'on account of my heart. It's weak, and the doctor expressly forbade any form of excitement or violent exercise. If it wasn't for that——'

He sat down on a corner of the bed.

'I haven't fought for years,' said Mr Dick with spirit; 'but I'm not going to be bullied by a damned Irish doctor. Come on.'

The speech was worthy of a man who had once at least felt the blood of the ancient Berserkers coursing through his veins. It was followed by prompt action. He took off his coat. Patsy Devlin spat on his hands and then rubbed them together.

'Mr Dick,' said Dr O'Grady, 'I don't want to have you smashed up, partly because from what you've told us about your wife I expect she'd be sorry, and partly because it'd be a nuisance to me to have to fit you together again. If you don't sit down on that bed, I'll ring the bell for the Emperor and get him to take away your clothes. You didn't like going about in nothing but your shirt yesterday evening. Just recollect that, and be careful.'

Mr Dick thought better of his resolution. It may have been the business-like way in which Patsy spat on his hands which daunted him, or it may have been Dr O'Grady's second and very horrible threat. He sat down sulkily beside Mr Sanders.

'Now,' said Dr O'Grady, 'I'm going to speak plainly to you for your own good. You've behaved uncommonly badly since you came here. You've sulked and you've whimpered, and you've raved in such a way as to make Patsy Devlin and me quite uncomfortable. We made every excuse for you yesterday afternoon. We recognized that Mr Dick couldn't be expected to be cheerful when he hadn't got any trousers. We knew that what had happened would upset Mr Sanders' heart and bring on palpitations. We did our best to make things easy for you. When the assistant anarchists brought up your beds, we made them for you, and allowed you to get into them, although it was barely five o'clock, and the habit of going to bed at that hour is most unsociable. Patsy brought your tea over to you later on before he drank a drop himself, to save you the trouble of getting out of bed. That was pure kindness of heart on Patsy's part, and you didn't so much as say "thank you".'

'They did not,' said Patsy, who stood behind the bed with sleeves still rolled up; 'and it will be long enough before I do the like again.'

'After tea,' said Dr O'Grady, 'I sent for the Emperor and persuaded him to let Mr Dick have his clothes back. I needn't have done that. It didn't matter to me if he had to go about stark naked for the rest of his natural life. Did you show any gratitude this morning? Not a bit. You sulked and whimpered again in the most unbearable manner. We put up with it. We tried to cheer you. There was an egg short at breakfast. Who did without? Patsy again; although he deserved an egg a great deal more than either of you. When breakfast was over, I suggested that we should all join in the game of flipping pennies across the table. I didn't do that because I wanted to play. As a matter of fact, I don't usually play in the morning; I read. Patsy will bear me out in that. I was prepared to sacrifice my own time and inclination to amuse you. How did you receive the proposal? You sulked again.'

'I was brought up strictly,' said Mr Sanders; 'I belong to the Free Kirk, and my conscience will not allow me to gamble.'

'That,' said Dr O'Grady, 'is a paltry excuse, which you ought to be ashamed to make. No man could be brought up to think it wrong to flip pennies. Besides, what is it that's wrong about gambling? It's the excitement created by the element of risk associated with all gambling. Now, in this case, as you know perfectly well, there would have been no excitement because there was no element of risk. The thing was a dead certainty. Patsy would have given you ten points in every game and beaten the head off you. If you had to make an excuse, why didn't you trot out your weak heart again? That would have been more reasonable. When you wouldn't play that, I proposed another game, called Moggy, at which you wouldn't have had a chance of winning either. You refused it too. Then I said that if you liked we'd have a debate on Home Rule or Tariff Reform. I said that you two could choose your own side and that Patsy and I would take the other, whatever it was. I thought that would interest you. It would have bored both Patsy and me frightfully; but we were prepared to put up with that for your sakes.'

'How could you expect us to take an interest in Tariff Reform,' said Mr Dick, 'when our minds were full of——'

'Patsy,' said Dr O'Grady, 'if that man mentions his wife again, hit him with the flat of your hand on the side of the head. Now go on, Mr Dick.'

'When—when we were imprisoned,' said Mr Dick.

'That ought not to have stopped you,' said Dr O'Grady. 'The great problems of your country's welfare ought to come before considerations of your personal convenience. Think of the ancient Romans. Remember Horatius, and Coriolanus, and the fellow that jumped into the hole in the Forum. That's the way you ought to be behaving instead of grumbling and growling. Now I'm going to give you another chance. If you choose to behave like reasonable human beings, well and good. Patsy and I will do everything in our power to make your stay here pleasant for you. If you won't, you shan't have a bite or sup until you do. I'll give you three minutes by my watch to make up your minds. Will you or will you not be sociable and pleasant? Will you join us in a game of Hunt the Slipper? Come over to the window, Patsy, and leave them to make up their minds together.'

Patsy and Dr O'Grady stood looking out at the yard; the doctor held his watch in his hand; there was dead silence in the room.

'One minute gone,' said Dr O'Grady.

There was a sound of whispering which ceased abruptly.

'Two minutes gone.'

There was more whispering. Then Mr Sanders spoke.

'Don't choose such a silly game,' he said. 'We can't play Hunt the Slipper. We really can't. Dick says he'd rather starve.'

'I'm not particular about what game you choose,' said Dr O'Grady, 'so long as it's a possible game. There's no use your saying golf or cricket or lawn tennis, because we've no way of playing them here. You can have Drop the Handkerchief, if you like, or Oranges and Lemons.'

This time there was a good deal of whispering, a kind of debate conducted with great earnestness.

'I'll play Hop Scotch, if you like,' said Mr Sanders; 'but Dick won't.'

'Never mind about Mr Dick,' said the doctor. He'll join in when he sees how pleasant it is. You can play Hop Scotch, I suppose, Patsy?'

'I cannot,' said Patsy. 'I never heard tell of it.'

'I can't either,' said the doctor. 'But it'll be all right: Mr Sanders will teach us.'

'I shall want a piece of chalk,' said Mr Sanders.

'There's no chalk here,' said Dr O'Grady. 'Will nothing else do you? What's the chalk for?'

'I have to mark out a figure on the boards,' said Mr Sanders.

'I've a small bottle of Condy's Fluid in my bag,' said the doctor, 'that I carry about with me for disinfecting my hands. You could manage with it, I dare say.'

'You can stain the floor with Condy's Fluid,' said Mr Dick, who was really a sociable man, and was beginning to be interested in the proceedings. 'When we were first married and went into our new house, my wife——'

'Now, don't start talking about your wife,' said Dr O'Grady, 'just as you're beginning to cheer up. You'll upset yourself again.'

Mr Sanders went down on his hands and knees. He made a little pool of Condy's Fluid on the floor and drew lines from it with his forefinger. The rest of the party watched with great interest. Suddenly he stopped and knelt bolt upright.

'What's that noise?' he said.

'I didn't hear any noise,' said Dr O'Grady. 'There wasn't any noise. Go on Hop Scotching.'

'There was a noise. I heard it. A noise like a fall. I have very sharp hearing.'

'That always goes with a weak heart,' said Dr O'Grady. 'But——'

He stopped abruptly. This time there was an unmistakable noise, a shout uttered somewhere in the lower part of the house, which reached even the remote room where the captives were. They drew together and waited, breathless. Mr Sanders grew very white.

'They're fighting downstairs,' he said.

'Perhaps the police have come,' said Mr Dick. 'Perhaps we shall be rescued. I knew that my wife would do everything to find me. I knew she would find me.'

'You didn't seem to think so yesterday,' said Dr O'Grady. 'And I wouldn't make too sure now, if I were you. If they are fighting downstairs, and I can't hear plainly enough to be certain——'

'I can,' said Mr Sanders.

'I expect,' said Dr O'Grady, 'that the Emperor will get the best of it. He'll probably be in on us here in a minute or two as proud as Punch at having bagged another chance traveller. If the Emperor has a fault at all, it's his extraordinary fondness for kidnapping people. I can't think why he does it.'

'They're coming upstairs,' said Mr Sanders. 'I hear them distinctly.'

'They are,' said Dr O'Grady; ' a whole lot of people. I wonder who he has got this time.'

The door of the room was unlocked. There was a short scuffle outside, and then Sergeant Farrelly and Constable Cole were thrust in. They both looked as if they had been roughly handled. The sergeant's tunic was torn, his right eye was beginning to swell, and there was blood on his lower lip. Mr Red, looking very grim and determined, stalked into the room behind them.

'Emperor,' said Dr O'Grady, 'this is too much. I complained to you yesterday about the habit you have got into of thrusting strange people in on top of me and Patsy. I put up with the last two, but this is more than I am going to stand.'

'They remain here,' said Mr Red, 'as captives.'

'Not at all,' said Dr O'Grady. 'Think it over, Emperor, and you'll come to see that you can't possibly leave them here. You are an anarchist, an anti-military anarchist. You've often told me so yourself. Now, an anarchist, as I understand his position, is absolutely pledged to every kind of social reform. Whatever anybody else may do, an anarchist can't consistently go in for the overcrowding of tenement houses, or tolerate insanitary persons. You see that, don't you? If ever it got out that you'd shut up six men in one room and kept them there, your reputation would be gone. There wouldn't be a decent anarchist anywhere in the world who'd recognize you as belonging to his party or so much as speak to you. You'd be a sort of Suraja Dowlah with a horrible Black Hole of Calcutta story cropping up against you at every turn. You simply must give these two men—— Oh, you're going, are you? Very well. But think over what I've said. You'll realize that I'm right.'

Mr Red shut the door and locked it. Sergeant Farrelly turned fiercely on Constable Cole.

'You born fool,' he said, 'why didn't you strike him when I had him down?'

'I'd have——'

'I suppose it was planning a stratagem you were,' said the sergeant, 'instead of striking when you got the chance.'

'I'd have broke his head,' said Constable Cole, 'if so be I'd struck him and me in the rage I was in at the time. How would I know but that it might be murder?'

'Serve you right if he broke yours,' said the sergeant.

'Come now,' said Dr O'Grady, 'there's no use making a fuss. You put up a middling good fight to judge by the look of you, and you ought to be content. None of the rest of us did as much.'

'Is that yourself, doctor?' said the sergeant.

'It is.'

'And, by the holy,' said Constable Cole, 'he has Patsy Devlin along with him!'

'And us thinking that the two of yez was off to America,' said the sergeant.

'I heard that you thought I'd gone,' said Dr O'Grady; 'but what made you suspect poor Patsy?'

'Hadn't he the funds collected for the sports?' said the sergeant.

'Be damn!' said Patsy, 'but that wasn't the cause of my going off, and well you know it, sergeant. It's little call you have to be saying the like of that about me, and you out after me at the time for the murder of the doctor. Wasn't that enough for you to be saying, without the other?'

'My wife?' said Mr Dick. 'Did you see her? Was she well?'

'She's distressed,' said the sergeant. 'The whole of them's

232

distressed, and small blame to them. I couldn't rightly tell this minute which of the ladies was your wife; but they were all round at the barrack this morning, and it would have gone to your heart to see the way they were.'

'As we're on the subject of ladies,' said Dr O'Grady, 'I suppose Miss Blow is out after me. I heard from Patsy that she'd arrived in Clonmore.'

'You may say she is,' said the sergeant. 'She has the officer's heart fair broke, pursuing him here and there, and not letting him rest in his bed at night the way he'd have us all scouring the country for your dead body.'

'And was it looking for me that brought you here, sergeant?' said Dr O'Grady.

'It was after they left the barrack,' said the sergeant, 'that the ladies went up to the Castle—Jimmy O'Loughlin's boy showing them the way—thinking that maybe, being a magistrate, Lord Manton would help them to find yez. What happened there I couldn't say; but it wasn't long after us eating our dinner when the officer came down and Lord Manton along with him and Miss Blow and the other ladies. Such language you never heard. There was one lady, tall she was, and dark, with a kind of grey dress on her, and a big umbrella under her arm with a stone knob on the end of the handle of it——'

'My aunt, I think,' said Mr Sanders.

'She might be. Anyway, barring the doctor's young lady, she was the worst of them for wanting to have Mr Red hanged for murdering the lot of yez.'

'I wouldn't wonder if he was hanged,' said Constable Cole, 'the way he's conducting himself. It's scandalous.'

'The orders I got,' went on Sergeant Farrelly, 'was to proceed to Rosivera, and ask Mr Red whether he'd noticed two Members of Parliament going by his gate on bicycles the day before.'

'And not to be in too great a hurry over the job,' said Constable Cole, 'because you was only doing it to satisfy the ladies.'

'Whisht!' said the sergeant; 'what call have you to be repeating confidential orders? So we came along——'

'Wait a minute,' said Dr O'Grady. 'How did you get off without taking Miss Blow with you? I'd have expected her to insist on going too.'

'She did,' said the sergeant; 'and it was only by means of a stratagem we got clear of her. It was Constable Cole invented the stratagem. He's great at that.'

'How did he manage?'

'Never mind about the stratagem,' said Mr Sanders; 'go on with your narrative.'

'I'll tell you about it after,' said the sergeant to Dr O'Grady in a whisper. Then he went on delivering himself of his tale very much as if he were giving evidence in a court of law.

'We reached Rosivera at half-past three P.M. We then knocked at the door and asked for Mr Red. We stepped into the hall of the house, Constable Cole being about two paces behind me. A tall man with a black beard, whom I can identify and swear to if necessary, came out of a door on the left, and without warning struck at my head with a stick. I aimed a blow at him with my fist, not having time to draw my baton, and knocked him down. I was then engaged by two other men. One of them was Mr Red, to whom I am prepared to swear. I shouted to Constable Cole to strike the man on the ground with his baton, in order to keep him quiet. Constable Cole did not obey my order.'

'I did not,' said Constable Cole; 'sure I might have killed him.'

'We were then overpowered,' said the sergeant, 'the man whom I knocked down coming to the assistance of his comrades. That's all, gentlemen.'

'I suppose,' said Mr Dick, 'that your officer will immediately telegraph for the military?'

'He might,' said the sergeant; 'but he won't do it sooner than tomorrow, anyway. He won't be expecting us home till late tonight.'

'I must warn the Emperor,' said Dr O'Grady. 'He had better clear out at once. I shouldn't like any harm to happen to the Emperor, and I know he hates soldiers. His whole life is given up to the destruction of standing armies. He'd break his heart if the military captured him in the end.'

'Do you mean to say that you intend——' said Mr Sanders.

'Of course I do,' said Dr O'Grady. 'The Emperor is a thoroughly decent sort, and has always treated me well. I'm not going to allow him to be bullied simply to gratify your passion for revenge. You pretend you think it wrong to gamble, but you're not above entertaining a spite against the poor Emperor and wanting to stick a knife into him. I can tell you, Mr Sanders, that sort of spirit is a jolly sight more unchristian than losing a few pence to Patsy Devlin over an innocent game.'

'The police,' said Mr Sanders confidently, 'will see that you do not assist this criminal to escape from justice.'

He looked at Sergeant Farrelly as he spoke. The sergeant scratched his head.

'Tell me this now,' he said to Dr O'Grady; 'is this any kind of League work?'

'It is not,' said the doctor. 'I don't suppose the Emperor ever heard of the League till I mentioned to him the other day that Patsy was a member of it.'

'If it's not the League,' said the sergeant, 'and if the doctor will answer for it that the man's a respectable man——'

'He is,' said the doctor. 'Why, my goodness, sergeant, he owns a motor car. You've seen it yourself, a remarkably fine motor car; one that couldn't have cost less than eight hundred pounds.'

'I don't know,' said the sergeant, 'that there's any call for me to interfere with the doctor in the matter. It would be a queer thing now, and a thing that wouldn't suit me at all, if I was to be preventing the doctor from speaking to a friend of his anyway that pleases him.'

235

'He attacked you,' said Mr Sanders; 'he knocked you down. He has imprisoned you, and yet you say——'

'If he's brought up before the Petty Sessions,' said the sergeant, 'I'll tell what he's done; but till he is I don't see what right I have to put the handcuffs on the doctor on account of what might be no more than some kind of a joke that's passing between him and another gentleman. . . .'

25

At ten o'clock next morning Jimmy O'Loughlin entered the commercial room of his hotel. Miss Blow was breakfasting by herself. Miss Farquharson, who had finished her breakfast an hour earlier, was writing letters at one end of the long table, having folded back the white cloth. Mrs Dick and Mrs Sanders were still in their bedrooms, mourning for their husbands.

'There's five police after coming into the town from Ballymoy,' said Jimmy excitedly; 'and it's what I'm after hearing from Moriarty that there's more expected.'

Miss Blow looked up from her breakfast. Her face expressed irritation and incredulity.

'It's the truth I'm telling you,' said Jimmy. 'Begad, but Mr Goddard's the fine man.'

'You told us last night,' said Miss Farquharson, 'that Mr Goddard had vanished like every one else. Has he appeared again?'

'He never was lost, thanks be to God! He was up with Lord

Manton beyond at the Castle, devising plans and concocting stratagems for the settling of the matter that's been troubling you; and settled it'll be now the one way or the other.'

'I know the sort of plans he and Lord Manton would be likely to devise,' said Miss Blow, scornfully. 'I've had some experience of them.'

She poured out a cup of tea as she spoke and devoted herself to her breakfast. Bridgy burst into the room. She appeared to be in a condition of violent excitement.

'There's four police on a car,' she said, 'driving up to the barrack, and two more along with them on bicycles.'

'Is that four more on top of the first five?' asked Jimmy O'Loughlin.

'It is, it is,' said Bridgy. 'The Lord save us and help us! There'd hardly be more of them if there was to be a Member of Parliament making speeches about the land!'

'There now,' said Jimmy O'Loughlin, reproachfully, to Miss Blow. 'What did I tell you? Sure, Mr Goddard's as fine a man as e'er a one that's in it. It's himself will do a job in style when once he takes it in hand at all. That's eleven men, and Constable Moriarty makes twelve, and there was a sergeant with the first lot that I seen myself. Was there e'er a sergeant on the other car, Bridgy?'

'There was,' said Bridgy. 'I took notice of him passing, and one of them two that came on bicycles had two stripes on his arm.'

'That makes two sergeants and an acting sergeant,' said Jimmy O'Loughlin. 'What more would you expect? What more would anybody want, unless it would be a gunboat sent round from Cork? And that's what you could hardly expect, unless it might be for an eviction on one of the islands.'

'I'll see what all these men are going to do,' said Miss Blow, 'before I give an opinion about them. I've been——'

'Here's Mr Goddard himself,' said Jimmy O'Loughlin, who was standing near the window, 'and his lordship along with him. And they have the big waggonette from the castle and the dog-cart with the yellow cob in it. Be damn, but it's great!'

Miss Farquharson stood up and looked out of the window. Miss Blow, obstinately sceptical, continued to eat her breakfast. Mr Goddard and Lord Manton entered the room.

'Ladies,' said Mr Goddard. 'In a quarter of an hour we start for Rosivera.'

'At the head of a small army,' said Lord Manton. 'Twelve men armed with carbines, not counting Mr Goddard, who wears a sword.'

'Fifteen men,' said Mr Goddard. 'I'm expecting three more. They may arrive at any minute.'

'I suppose,' said Miss Blow, 'that this is some new kind of trick.'

'Come and see,' said Mr Goddard. 'Lord Manton has placed his waggonette at your disposal. We invite your presence. We insist upon it.'

'My niece and Mrs Dick,' said Miss Farquharson, 'are still in their bedrooms.'

'Get them out,' said Lord Manton, 'as quickly as possible. There is no time to be lost. Military expeditions of this sort cannot possibly be delayed.'

'If so be,' said Jimmy O'Loughlin, 'that you'll be wanting me, as a magistrate, to be taking depositions or the like——'

'We don't absolutely require you,' said Lord Manton; 'but we'll be glad to have you up with us.'

'It'll be better, then,' said Jimmy, 'if I go upstairs and put on a decent coat and shave myself. Bridgy, will you run like a good girl and get me a sup of hot water?'

'You may change your coat,' said Mr Goddard, 'but you can't shave. There isn't time.'

Miss Blow and Miss Farquharson left the room together.

'Would you have any objection to telling me,' said Jimmy O'Loughlin, 'what is it that you're thinking of doing?'

'It's Lord Manton's plan,' said Mr Goddard, 'not mine. The

fact is, we're going to Rosivera to marry Mr Red either to Miss Blow or Miss Farquharson.'

'And is that the reason you have the police gathered from the four corners of the county?'

'It is,' said Mr Goddard.

'I wouldn't wonder but what you're right. It's ten to one he won't care for the notion; not but what Miss Blow is a fine-looking young lady, and that's what I've always said since the first time ever I set eyes on her.'

The street of Clonmore, the single street which runs from end to end of the village, presented a most unusual appearance when Miss Blow, followed by the other three ladies, emerged from the hotel. A long line of vehicles stretched from the door of the post-office to the barrack. There were two cars, each holding four policemen. They had their carbines between their knees and presented a most warlike and determined appearance. Next came a third car, Jimmy O'Loughlin's, with two policemen on one side of it, the side left vacant being intended for the accommodation of Mr Goddard. Behind it was Lord Manton's dog-cart. Jimmy O'Loughlin was on the back seat, Lord Manton sat beside the groom in front. Next came the waggonette with Mrs Patsy Devlin in it. The acting sergeant and the constable who had arrived on bicycles stood beside their machines immediately behind the waggonette. They formed a kind of rear-guard, and could be counted on to frustrate any attempt which Mr Red might make to attack the party from behind.

An eager crowd thronged the footpaths and broke into a cheer when the ladies appeared.

'Miss Blow, Miss Farquharson and ladies——' said Mr Goddard, when the noise of the cheering had subsided.

'We thought you were murdered too,' said Mrs Dick.

'Kindly do not interrupt me,' said Mr Goddard. He felt that he was at last in a position to assert himself even in the face of Miss Blow. A man requires self-confidence when he is in command of an armed force.

'We start,' he said, 'for Rosivera, to discover whether Mr Red, the man Red, as he has been well described, the tenant of that house, has anything to do with the extraordinary series of disappearances which have disturbed the peace of this neighbourhood.'

Lord Manton said, 'Hear, hear!' from his seat in the dog-cart, and the crowd cheered again.

'We invite your presence, ladies, and place the waggonette which you see at your disposal. When you are seated in it we start at once. God save the King!'

'Hear, hear!' said Lord Manton again.

The four ladies, a little bewildered by this oration, took their seats in the waggonette. Mr. Goddard got up on his car and gave the order to march. The expedition started.

An hour's steady driving brought the party to the top of the hill from which the gate of Rosivera is visible. Mr Goddard gave the order to halt. It was passed forward to the leading car, and the expedition came to a standstill on the summit of the hill. Mr Goddard got down from his car and walked up to Lord Manton.

'It's a damned awkward thing,' he said, 'to march up to a man's house at the head of a body of men like this.'

'Don't say you're thinking of going back,' said Lord Manton. 'It would be a shame to disappoint Miss Blow.'

'I'm not going back; but all the same it's awkward. What excuse shall I make?'

'If he's been kidnapping people,' said Lord Manton, 'he won't expect you to make any excuse.'

'Oh, of course, if he really has. But has he?'

'The only way of finding out for certain is to go and see. Miss Blow won't be satisfied with anything less.'

'Damn Miss Blow. Anyhow, we needn't drive up to the house as if we were a funeral.'

He gave an order to the police, who dismounted. Mr Goddard marched at the head of them down the hill. Lord Manton and Jimmy O'Loughlin followed. The ladies, led by Miss

Blow, also followed. At the gate of Rosivera, Mr Goddard halted his party. He ordered the police to remain outside the gate. He invited Lord Manton to accompany him to the house. Then with a glance at the ladies he told one of the sergeants not to allow any one else to pass the gate.

Miss Blow reached the bottom of the hill and prepared to follow Mr Goddard along the avenue. She was stopped by the sergeant. Suspecting some trick to be played on her at this last and critical moment, she suggested to Miss Farquharson that they should force their way through the cordon of police by making, all four of them, a simultaneous rush. Miss Farquharson refused to do anything of the sort, and gave it as her opinion that Mrs Sanders and Mrs Dick would be quite useless in a hand-to-hand conflict. Miss Blow left her, walked a little way across the road, crossed a ditch, and began to climb the wall which enclosed the Rosivera grounds. The police eyed her doubtfully. They did not want to lay violent hands on Miss Blow. They excused themselves to their own consciences. Their orders were to prevent her passing through the gate. Mr Goddard had said nothing about what was to be done if she climbed the wall.

Mr Goddard and Lord Manton surveyed the house. It looked peaceful, too peaceful. There was no sign of its being inhabited.

'Are you sure,' said Mr Goddard, 'that there's anybody here?'

'I'm not so sure,' said Lord Manton. 'I only know that I let the house to the man Red. He may or may not be living in it. I never saw him.'

Mr Goddard walked up to the door and knocked. There was no answer. He knocked again. Still there was no answer. He turned the handle and pushed. The door resisted his push. It was locked.

'What shall we do now?' he said to Lord Manton.

Then he caught sight of Miss Blow, who was crossing the gravel sweep.

'Go back,' he said; 'go back at once. This is no place for ladies.'

'I won't go back,' said Miss Blow. 'If I did you'd not enter the house at all. You would come back in ten minutes and say you had searched it and that there was nobody inside.'

'My dear Miss Blow,' said Lord Manton, 'Mr Goddard may perhaps deserve that, but surely I don't. Be just. Give me credit for common honesty.'

'I'm sorry I can't do that,' said Miss Blow.

'You might,' said Lord Manton. 'I gave you tea yesterday.'

'You can come with us if you like,' said Mr Goddard; 'but how do you propose to get in? The door is locked.'

'The top of that is open,' said Miss Blow, pointing with her finger to the window at the left side of the door, 'so I suppose the bottom can be pushed up.'

Mr Goddard felt like a burglar, which is an unpleasant sensation for a police officer, but one which he was getting gradually accustomed to. He had experienced it when he hid in the stable of Jimmy O'Loughlin's hotel and when he entered his own house by way of the back garden. He had experienced it when he drove out of Ballymoy in the early morning and when he tried to escape from Lord Manton's library. He had experienced it again when he had concealed himself in the Clonmore post-office. He opened the window and climbed in. Miss Blow followed him. Lord Manton, moving rather stiffly, for he was not used to climbing, followed her. They stood together in the dining-room.

'Dear me,' said Lord Manton, 'what a very remarkable taste Mr Red has in wall decoration! Yellow dragons on a crimson ground! Did you ever see anything like that before, Miss Blow?'

Miss Blow made no answer. She was opening the doors of the small cupboards in the sideboard, in the hope, perhaps, of discovering the mutilated remains of some of Mr Red's victims. She found nothing but empty bottles and some wine-glasses.

'Even the door,' said Lord Manton, 'has been painted, and

there is a large yellow dragon on it, a mother dragon with several young ones. You'd better follow her, Goddard.'

He added this hurriedly, and obviously did not refer to the female dragon. Miss Blow had opened the door and passed through it into the hall.

'The door opposite to you,' said Lord Manton, 'leads into the drawing-room.'

It did not look like a drawing-room when they entered it. A heavy deal table, like a carpenter's bench, stood in the middle of the floor, and on it were a number of curiously shaped metal flasks. There was a pile of long brass tubes in one corner of the room, which looked like empty cartridge cases, intended to contain ammunition for some very large gun. There were wooden shelves all round the walls stocked with thick glass bottles, such as are seen in chemists' shops, bottles with glass stoppers. In one corner the floor was charred, as if a fire had been lighted on it.

'Nobody here,' said Mr Goddard, looking round.

Lord Manton was staring curiously at the things about him. He picked up one of the brass tubes.

'A.M.B.A.,' he read. 'What do you suppose that means, Miss Blow? Hullo! She's gone again. After her Goddard! We can't allow her to escape. There may be an explosion at any moment. This place looks uncommonly explosive, and if she is shattered into little bits her father will hold us responsible.'

Miss Blow stood at the bottom of the stairs, listening intently.

'I hear a noise in the upper storey,' she said. 'The house isn't empty.'

Mr Goddard and Lord Manton listened.

'There is a noise,' said Lord Manton. 'Goddard, unsheathe your sword and proceed cautiously up the first flight of stairs. We will protect your rear.'

They reached the first floor of the house and the noise became much more plainly audible.

'It sounds to me,' said Lord Manton, 'as if Mr Red—the

man, Red, I mean—and his friends were having a hurdle race in the attics.'

'Go on,' said Miss Blow.

'Let us pause for a moment,' said Lord Manton, 'and consider the situation before we rush headlong into some unknown danger. I am inclined to think that several men are jumping hurdles, and from the occasional violence of the bumps I should say that one of them is a heavy man, much heavier than the others. Can you infer anything else from the noise we hear, Miss Blow? Or you, Goddard? Very well, if neither of you can, we may as well go on, bearing in mind that there are several men and that one of them is large.'

They climbed two more flights of stairs and reached the top storey of the house. The noise sounded very loud. Guided by it they reached the door of a room at the end of a passage. Mr Goddard knocked. There was no reply, for the noise inside was so great as to drown the knock.

'Go in,' said Miss Blow.

Mr Goddard turned the handle. 'The door is locked,' he said.

'The key is on the outside,' said Miss Blow. 'Turn it.'

'As landlord of the house,' said Lord Manton, 'allow me.'

He turned the key and flung open the door. Inside were Dr O'Grady, Mr Dick, Patsy Devlin, Sergeant Farrelly and Constable Cole. They were playing leapfrog. Mr Sanders sat on a bed in the corner and watched them. Dr O'Grady, executing a splendid bound over Sergeant Farrelly's broad back, landed on his feet opposite the door just as it opened.

'Adeline Maud,' he said, 'I'm delighted to see you. Have you been here long? I hope you weren't kept waiting at the door.'

26

'DEAR me!' said Lord Manton; 'all our lost sheep are found again. One, two, three, four, five, six. Yes, the whole six of you.'

'You're not dead,' said Miss Blow, clutching at Dr O'Grady's arm; 'you're not dead then, after all.'

'My wife,' said Mr Dick, 'my poor wife. Can any of you tell me——'

'Sergeant Farrelly,' said Mr Goddard, 'will you kindly explain how it is that I find you here playing leapfrog with——'

'I thought it was a hurdle race,' said Lord Manton. 'It sounded like a hurdle race.'

Sergeant Farrelly drew himself up to attention.

'In obedience to your orders, sir,' he said, 'Constable Cole and I proceeded to Rosivera on our bicycles, leaving Clonmore at a few minutes after twelve o'clock. Acting on instructions received, we rode as slowly as possible——'

'You can leave out that part,' said Mr Goddard, with a glance at Miss Blow, 'and go on.'

'We have been kidnapped and imprisoned here,' said Mr Sanders; 'and I demand that the police shall instantly pursue——'

'Lucius,' said Miss Blow, 'have you been imprisoned?'

'Certainly not,' said Dr O'Grady; 'we've been the guests of Mr Red; haven't we, Patsy?'

'We have, be damn!' said Patsy Devlin. 'What was there to hinder us going off any time we wanted?'

'I don't understand,' said Miss Blow.

'I demand——' said Mr Sanders again.

'We were prisoners,' said Mr Dick; 'and I join with my friend Sanders in insisting that the men who captured us shall be brought to justice. I insist upon it for the sake of my poor wife——'

'You shut up,' said Dr O'Grady. 'If either you or that ass Sanders says another word, I'll tell how you came to be here.'

'I demand——' said Mr Sanders.

'Very well,' said Dr O'Grady. 'Excuse me, Adeline Maud, but would you mind leaving the room for a moment? The story I have to tell is not exactly one for a lady to listen to.'

'If it's very improper,' said Lord Manton, 'perhaps I'd better go too. I was very carefully brought up when I was young.'

'It's simply this,' said Dr O'Grady, 'that Mr Dick was found by the Emperor bathing on the shore in company with——'

'I wasn't,' said Mr Dick.

'You may try to wriggle out of it now,' said Dr O'Grady, 'but you told me at the time that you were, and the other fellow, who says he's a Member of Parliament, but looks like a commercial traveller, was mending a bicycle for a lady who——'

'If these stories,' said Lord Manton, 'are the sort which are likely to break up the happiness of two homes, I hope you won't tell them. Mrs Dick and Mrs Sanders are outside as well as Miss Farquharson, who is an aunt.'

'I don't want to tell them,' said Dr O'Grady. 'I'd much rather keep them to myself. But I won't have the Emperor pursued.'

'Sergeant,' said Mr Goddard, 'proceed with your evidence, leaving out all the part about my orders.'

'Why?' said Miss Blow. 'Are you ashamed of your orders? What were they?'

'If you've anything to be ashamed of in the orders you gave, Goddard,' said Dr O'Grady, 'you'd better not have that story told either. I warn you fairly that if any attempt is made to molest the Emperor, I shall have those orders of yours, whatever they are, produced in court.'

'We might get on a little,' said Lord Manton, 'if some one would tell us who the Emperor is.'

'He's an anarchist,' said Mr Sanders.

'An anti-military anarchist, a most dangerous man,' added Mr Dick.

'I've warned you once already,' said Dr O'Grady, 'what will happen if you persist in talking that way. Even supposing the poor old Emperor is all you say, isn't it a great deal better to blow up a few armies, than to go about the country deceiving innocent women when each of you has a wife at home? Patsy Devlin will bear me out in saying that the Emperor is a most respectable man, large-hearted, generous to a fault; a little eccentric, perhaps, but a thoroughly good sort.'

'Do explain,' said Lord Manton, 'who the Emperor is, and how you and Patsy Devlin and the Members of Parliament and the police all come to be here, playing leapfrog in an attic.'

'The Emperor,' said Dr O'Grady, 'is Mr Red. He sent for me to attend a servant of his who had unfortunately scorched the back of his legs while assisting in some scientific experiments in the Chamber of Research.'

'The drawing-room?' asked Lord Manton.

'The room that used to be the drawing-room,' said Dr O'Grady. 'I have been in attendance on the man ever since, earning a fee of five pounds a day. That doesn't look as if I was badly treated, does it? Or as if I was kept here against my will? There's no other reason, so far, why the poor Emperor should be ruthlessly pursued, as these gentlemen suggest.'

'No,' said Lord Manton. 'So far his record is clear. Go on.'

'Patsy Devlin,' said Dr O'Grady, 'came here to take refuge from the police. He hadn't done anything particularly wrong, nothing worse than usual; but some one had put out the absurd story that he had murdered me, and advised him to fly to America.'

'I'm afraid that I was responsible for that,' said Lord Manton. 'I wanted——'

'Very well,' said Dr O'Grady. 'If the Emperor is pursued

and caught, that story will come out too. You will have to explain in open court why you treated Patsy Devlin in such a way.'

'And why you treated me as you did,' said Miss Blow.

'And why you treated Adeline Maud as you did,' said Dr O'Grady. 'I don't exactly know how you did treat her, but if you pursue the Emperor I'll insist on finding out.'

'I won't pursue him,' said Lord Manton. 'I promise not to. As a matter of fact, I don't want to pursue him in the least. He paid his rent in advance.'

'Patsy Devlin,' said Dr O'Grady, 'was sheltered, lodged, and fed by the Emperor, and has no complaint whatever to make. Have you, Patsy?'

'I have not. Only for him they'd have had me hanged for murdering you, doctor; which is what I wouldn't do, and never thought of.'

'And you don't want to have the Emperor pursued?'

'I do not,' said Patsy.

'We pass on,' said Dr O'Grady, 'to the case of the two Members of Parliament—if they are Members of Parliament. I don't want to make myself unnecessarily unpleasant, especially as I understand that their wives, their real wives, are waiting for them——'

'I protest——' said Mr Dick.

'I always told you, Goddard,' said Lord Manton, 'that there was something of this sort, something uncommonly fishy behind the disappearance of these two gentlemen. You'll recollect that. But I must say I didn't expect it to be as bad as this.'

'I protest,' said Mr Dick and Mr Sanders together.

'I need say no more about them,' said Dr O'Grady. The Emperor, out of sheer kindness of heart, saved them from what might have been a very ugly scandal. I don't want to drag the whole thing into the light of day; but if they insist upon the pursuit of the Emperor, I shall tell the truth so far as I know it, and the Emperor, when you catch him, will fill in the details.'

'There's nothing,' said Mr Dick, 'absolutely nothing——'

'There may be nothing,' said Lord Manton; 'but from the little I've heard I should say that Mrs Dick will have a distinct grievance; and as for your aunt, Mr Saunders—you know her better than I do, of course, but she doesn't strike me as the kind of lady who will treat the doctor's story as a mere trifle.'

'As to the police,' said Dr O'Grady, 'I don't profess to explain exactly how they came here. Goddard seems to have given them some very peculiar orders, orders that won't bear repeating. I don't want to probe into the secrets of the force. I have a respect for Sergeant Farrelly; I used to have a respect for Goddard——'

'You won't have any respect for him when you hear how he has treated me,' said Miss Blow.

'You hear that, Goddard?' said Dr O'Grady. 'Adeline Maud says you've been ill-treating her. That's a thing I can't stand and won't stand from any man living, and if you make the smallest attempt to annoy the Emperor in any way, I'll publish her story in the newspapers, and what's more, I'll hire the best barrister in Dublin to cross-examine you about the orders you gave to Sergeant Farrelly and Constable Cole.'

'What you suggest then,' said Lord Manton, 'is to leave the whole matter wrapped in a decent obscurity—to let the past bury its dead. I quite agree. None of us want our share in the proceedings of the last few days made public. But will Miss Blow consent to allow the man Red—it's her phrase, doctor, not mine, so don't be angry with it—to allow the man Red to escape scot free? After all, it was she who urged us on to have him hanged.'

'Adeline Maud,' said Dr O'Grady, 'has more sense than to quarrel with a man who has been paying me five pounds a day. He suggested four pounds at first; but he sprang it to a fiver the moment I made the suggestion.'

'Of course, if Miss Blow is satisfied——' said Lord Manton.

'She is,' said Dr O'Grady. 'Aren't you, Adeline Maud?'

'Now that I know you're safe——' said Miss Blow.

'In any case,' said Dr O'Grady, 'your pursuit would be quite useless. The Emperor started at ten o'clock last night in his motor car. It must be after twelve now, so he has fourteen hours start of you. By the time you get back to Clonmore and send off telegrams——'

'I shall insist,' said Mr Dick. 'I shall never consent——'

'You go out at once to your wife,' said Dr O'Grady. 'Didn't you hear Lord Manton say that she is outside waiting for you? You've been swaggering about the way you loved her ever since I first met you walking about with nothing on you but your shirt. I don't believe you care a pin about her. If you did, you'd be with her now, relieving her anxiety, instead of standing about here talking like a born fool. As I was saying, Goddard, by the time you've sent off telegrams——'

'I don't want to send off any more telegrams,' said Mr Goddard; 'I had enough of that yesterday.'

'In any case,' said Dr O'Grady, 'I don't think you'd catch him, when he'd have fifteen or sixteen hours' start of your telegrams. It was a good car, and I don't believe you so much as know the number of it.'

'The only thing that troubles me,' said Mr Goddard, 'is the Inspector-General. He'll be in Clonmore by this time.'

'Is he mixed up in it?'

'Yes,' said Lord Manton. 'He and the Lord Lieutenant and the Chief Secretary, and the Prime Minister; though I'm not quite sure about the Prime Minister. It's a State affair. The whole Empire is on the tip-toe of excited expectation to find out what has happened.'

'All you can do,' said Dr O'Grady, 'is to tell them the truth.'

'The truth?' said Lord Manton.

'Yes; the simple truth, just as I've told it to you; doing your best, of course, to spare Mr Sanders and Mr Dick, especially Mr Dick, on account of his poor wife.'

'I'm not sure,' said Mr Goddard, 'that they'd believe—I

mean to say, I'm not sure that I could venture to tell them the truth—that exact kind of truth, I mean.'

'If you don't care to tell it yourself,' said Dr O'Grady, 'get Jimmy O'Loughlin to tell it for you. He'd do it; wouldn't he, Patsy?'

'Be damn, but he would,' said Patsy Devlin. 'He'd tell it without as much as turning a hair, so soon as ever he knew what it was you wanted him to tell.'